Family Environment
and Borderline
Personality Disorder

Series

David Spiegel, M.D.
Series Editor

Family Environment and Borderline Personality Disorder

Edited by
Paul S. Links, M.D., M.Sc., F.R.C.P.(C)

Washington, DC
London

Copyright © 1990 American Psychiatric Press, Inc.
ALL RIGHTS RESERVED
Manufactured in the United States of America
First Edition   93 92 91 90 4 3 2 1

American Psychiatric Press, Inc., 1400 K St., N.W., Suite 1101, Washington, D.C. 20005

The paper used in this publication meets the minimum requirements of the American National Standard for Information Sciences — Permanence of Paper for Printed Library Materials, ANSI Z39.48 — 1984.   ∞

Library of Congress Cataloging-in-Publication Data

Family environment and borderline personality disorder/
edited by Paul S. Links. — 1st ed.
        p.   cm. — (Progress in psychiatry series)
    Includes bibliographical references.
    ISBN 0-88048-188-9 (alk. paper)
    1. Borderline personality disorder — Etiology.
    2. Problem families. I. Links, Paul S. II. Series.
    [DNLM: 1. Family. 2. Personality Disorder — Etiology.
WM 190 F198]
RC569.5.B67F36   1990
616.85'852 — dc20
DNLM/DLC
for Library of Congress   89-18574
                                                              CIP

British Library Cataloguing in Publication Data

A CIP record is available from the British Library.

Contents

Contributors

Ingrid Boiago, B.A., R.N.
Research Nurse, Department of Psychiatry, McMaster University, Hamilton, Ontario, Canada

Frances R. Frankenburg, M.D.
Clinical Instructor in Psychiatry, Harvard Medical School, Boston, Massachusetts; Assistant Psychiatrist, McLean Hospital, Belmont, Massachusetts

Sonya Goodrich, Ph.D.
Psychologist, Department of Psychiatry, University of Michigan, Ann Arbor, Michigan

John G. Gunderson, M.D.
Associate Professor of Psychiatry, Harvard Medical School, Boston, Massachusetts; Director of Psychotherapy and Psychosocial Research Program, McLean Hospital, Belmont, Massachusetts

Gail Huxley, R.N.
Research Nurse, Department of Psychiatry, McMaster University, Hamilton, Ontario, Canada

Paul S. Links, M.D., M.Sc., F.R.C.P.(C)
Director of Research, Department of Psychiatry, Hamilton Civic Hospitals; Associate Professor, Department of Psychiatry, McMaster University, Hamilton, Ontario, Canada

Margaret F. Marino, M.Ed.
Clinical Fellow in Psychology, Harvard Medical School and Massachusetts General Hospital, Boston, Massachusetts

Elsa Marziali, Ph.D.
Associate Professor, Faculty of Social Work, Assistant Professor, Faculty of Medicine, University of Toronto, Toronto, Ontario, Canada

Janice E. Mitton, R.N., B.A., M.H.Sc.
Research Nurse, Department of Psychiatry, McMaster University, Hamilton, Ontario, Canada

Heather Munroe Blum, Ph.D.
Dean and Professor of Social Work, University of Toronto, Toronto; Associate Member, Departments of Psychiatry and Clinical Epidemiology and Biostatistics, McMaster University, Hamilton, Ontario, Canada

Susan N. Ogata, Ph.D.
Clinical Psychologist, Bayshore Medical Group, Redondo Beach, California

Joel Paris, M.D.
Institute of Community and Family Psychiatry, Sir Mortimer B. Davis — Jewish General Hospital; Associate Professor of Psychiatry, McGill University, Montreal, Quebec, Canada

Elizabeth O. Schwartz, M.S.
Research Assistant, Psychosocial Research Program, McLean Hospital, Belmont, Massachusetts

Barry M. Segal, M.B., B.Ch.
Staff Psychiatrist, Hamilton Psychiatric Hospital; Assistant Professor, Department of Psychiatry, McMaster University, Hamilton, Ontario, Canada

Kenneth R. Silk, M.D.
Clinical Assistant Professor of Psychiatry, Department of Psychiatry, University of Michigan, Ann Arbor, Michigan

Meir Steiner, M.D., Ph.D.
Head, Clinical Studies Program, St. Joseph's Hospital; Professor, Departments of Psychiatry and Biomedical Sciences, McMaster University, Hamilton, Ontario, Canada

Michael H. Stone, M.D.
Professor of Clinical Psychiatry, Columbia College of Physicians and Surgeons; Visiting Professor of Psychiatry, Albert Einstein College of Medicine, New York, New York

Mary C. Zanarini, Ed.D.
Instructor in Psychology, Harvard Medical School, Boston, Massachusetts; Assistant Psychologist, McLean Hospital, Belmont, Massachusetts

Introduction to the Progress in Psychiatry Series

The Progress in Psychiatry Series is designed to capture in print the excitement that comes from assembling a diverse group of experts from various locations to examine in detail the newest information about a developing aspect of psychiatry. This series emerged as a collaboration between the American Psychiatric Association's (APA) Scientific Program Committee and the American Psychiatric Press, Inc. Great interest is generated by a number of the symposia presented each year at the APA annual meeting, and we realized that much of the information presented there, carefully assembled by people who are deeply immersed in a given area, would unfortunately not appear together in print. The symposia sessions at the annual meetings provide an unusual opportunity for experts who otherwise might not meet on the same platform to share their diverse viewpoints for a period of 3 hours. Some new themes are repeatedly reinforced and gain credence, while in other instances disagreements emerge, enabling the audience and now the reader to reach informed decisions about new directions in the field. The Progress in Psychiatry Series allows us to publish and capture some of the best of the symposia and thus provide an in-depth treatment of specific areas that might not otherwise be presented in broader review formats.

Psychiatry is by nature an interface discipline, combining the study of mind and brain, of individual and social environments, of the humane and the scientific. Therefore, progress in the field is rarely linear—it often comes from unexpected sources. Further, new developments emerge from an array of viewpoints that do not necessarily provide immediate agreement but rather expert examination of the issues. We intend to present innovative ideas and data that will enable you, the reader, to participate in this process.

We believe the Progress in Psychiatry Series will provide you with an opportunity to review timely new information in specific fields of interest as they are developing. We hope you find that the excitement of the presentations is captured in the written word and that this book proves to be informative and enjoyable reading.

David Spiegel, M.D.
Series Editor
Progress in Psychiatry Series

Progress in Psychiatry Series Titles

Introduction

> Children begin by loving their parents; as they grow older
> they judge them; sometimes they forgive them.
>
> Oscar Wilde *The Picture of Dorian Gray*

T he impact of the family environment on some of our most
severely disturbed patients has been of interest to clinicians
and researchers for decades. Like the growth from childhood to
adulthood, the study of the etiologic factors of borderline personality
disorder is a dynamic process evolving with time. The purpose of
this volume is to document how current research efforts have re-
defined our understanding of the impact of the family environment
on borderline personality disorder, and to lay a foundation for future
research studies carried out in this area.

The chapters in this volume have been organized to illustrate the
methodologic approaches that have recently been employed to address etiologic hypotheses related to borderline personality disorder.
In Chapter 1, Drs. Links and Munroe Blum present an overview of
empirical studies done over the past decade that have examined the
relationship between family environment and the development of
borderline personality disorder. Out of this review, specific etiologic
models are proposed and opportunities for further research are outlined. In Chapter 2, Dr. Segal reviews some of the traditional etiologic
theories that have developed out of observing individual patients in
analytic therapy. These models are reviewed to contrast them to one
another, and it is against this background of theoretical constructs
that most other empirical studies have been done.

Drs. Marziali and Munroe Blum, in Chapter 3, discuss the interpersonal phenomena characteristic of borderline pathology. These
authors identify how improvement in our methodologic approach
to these aspects could advance our examination of etiologic and
treatment issues.

In Chapter 4, Dr. Zanarini and her colleagues examine the family history of borderline patients compared to near-neighbor personality disorder controls. The family history method allows for an examination of both the validity of this psychiatric diagnosis and the need for the development of hypotheses about the possible inheritability of certain traits that may define borderline personality disorder.

In Chapter 5, Dr. Ogata and her colleagues present a case control design that compares borderline and depressed patients on various aspects of their childhood experience. In a similar fashion, Dr. Links and his colleagues, in Chapter 6, utilize a case control design to examine two specific models that have been used to explain the development of borderline personality disorder. The last two studies in this volume take a somewhat different tack by examining the impact of developmental factors on the outcome of borderline personality disorder. Both Dr. Paris and Dr. Stone examine how developmental factors explain the course and outcome of this disorder. In the final chapter, Dr. Gunderson comments on the findings from this collection of research and presents an outline of how these studies can provide a foundation for the next generation of research into the etiology of borderline personality disorder.

Writing this introduction at the kitchen table in my family home reminds me of how our lives are formed and facilitated by this environment. The sounds, the activity, the energy keep me involved without being a total distraction. My own experiences make it necessary for me to acknowledge my parents, Harold and Margaret, my wife Michelle, and my sons Braedan and Duncan, who have formed and facilitated me.

Others instrumental in seeing this work to completion include the following: Ingrid Boiago and Kerry Atack, who provided hours of hard work and support, and Drs. Heather Munroe Blum, Meir Steiner, and Ed Kingstone, who have been particularly instrumental in creating and supporting the Borderline Studies Group at McMaster University, Hamilton, Ontario, Canada. Many colleagues from the Borderline Studies Group have participated in the research, and we appreciate their contributions that have made this and other reports possible. We acknowledge the Ontario Mental Health Foundation, which was responsible for supporting some of the research presented in this volume.

Paul S. Links, M.D., M.Sc., F.R.C.P.(C)

Chapter 1

Family Environment and Borderline Personality Disorder: Development of Etiologic Models

Paul S. Links, M.D., M.Sc., F.R.C.P.(C)
Heather Munroe Blum, Ph.D.

Chapter 1

Family Environment and Borderderline Personality Disorder: Development of Etiologic Models

The etiology of most major psychiatric disorders remains to be determined. When disorders are chronic and have an insidious onset, the study of causation and the temporal relationship between purported etiologic factors and the outcome of interest is extremely difficult. When the disorders involve impairment in patterns of perceiving, relating to, and thinking about one's environment and oneself (American Psychiatric Association 1987), the complexities of measuring and defining the outcome and the chain of events leading to that outcome are readily apparent. When the boundary between normality and disorder is ill defined, the elucidation of specific etiologic factors appears impossible. These are some of the dilemmas facing the elaboration of etiologic hypotheses for personality disorders, including borderline personality disorder (BPD). However, untangling the etiologic threads leading to BPD and/or predicting the course and outcome of the disorder are necessary so that meaningful treatment and preventive strategies can be tested and proven. The elaboration of hypotheses relating to disorder onset and course must be seen as a dynamic process. This chapter will focus on recent changes in etiologic formulation and indicate how methodologic advances may yield further progress.

The objective of this chapter is to follow the development of theoretical models of psychosocial causation of BPD with an emphasis on the role of the family environment. We will begin by briefly reviewing some of the theories that were expounded by psychodynamic theorists. These theories predominately came from observing a handful of patients in intensive psychotherapy and inferring from the patients' recollections of the family environment. Gunderson, the father of the modern borderline concept, and other investigators have collected empirical data attempting to address the original dynamic hypotheses. Recent and related areas of family research are having an impact on the refinement of theories of causation and will be discussed. These areas include research on the effects of physical and sexual abuse in childhood, living with parents with psychiatric illness, and early maternal/paternal separation and loss. Finally, we will review the major methodologic advances in the investigation of family factors that have come from the study of the family and schizophrenia, and we will discuss their potential contributions to the study of BPD.

PREVIOUS STUDIES OF FAMILY ENVIRONMENT

Although a review of the psychodynamic literature and the etiologic theories growing out of this work is beyond the focus of this chapter (see Chapter 2 for a full discussion), a consensus from this literature appears to place weight on the role of abnormal development during Mahler's (1971) separation-individuation phase as a contributor to the development of BPD. However, variations on this theme are clearly evident. Kernberg (1984) theorized that borderline pathology was a consequence of a developmental failure occurring after self-object differentiation but before the development of object constancy. Adler (1985) focused on the failure of the development of object constancy and the child's inability to move beyond evocative memory. Although extrapolations from infant observations to adult pathology should be viewed with extreme skepticism, Shapiro (1978) indicated that such theories have had an important impact on helping therapists to listen better to elements that patients produce in therapy, to develop more accurate empathic responses, and to provide a means to organize the borderline patient's chaotic experience.

Stone (1981) provided an important impetus to the evolution of the borderline syndrome by identifying its close boundary with affective disorders and by pointing to the heterogeneous nature of the syndrome. He outlined a theory highlighting the interplay between inborn vulnerability, perhaps to affective disorders, and developmental traumata. Four pathways or tracks were expounded to demonstrate a possible combination of factors leading to borderline versus neurotic disorders. The first track concerns an individual with high degrees of genetic vulnerability who, even with nurturing and protective parents, develops borderline disorder. The second track involves a vulnerable child who escapes developing the borderline syndrome because of excellent parenting that protects the child. The third track follows a child with moderate vulnerability who, because of poor parenting, develops borderline psychopathology. Finally, Stone describes the fourth track: "abysmal, ego-crushing psychosocial environments (chronic child abuse, severe parental deprivation, as examples) swamp a child's developing psychic resources, even in the absence of any discernible vulnerability, and limits his function, as he approaches adult life, to the borderline level" (Stone 1981, p. 7). Stone's theorizing exemplifies the need to move beyond earlier formulations by including the borderline condition's biological relationship to Axis I, by illustrating the heterogeneous routes leading to borderline psychopathology, by suggesting that protective factors may interplay with risk factors leading to the borderline outcome, and by introducing "ego-crushing" traumata as mechanisms leading to the borderline disorder.

All formulations of the etiology of BPD have stressed the importance of the family environment. In the same volume as Stone's article, Gunderson and Englund (1981) reviewed the literature up to 1978 that characterized the families of borderline patients. These studies were largely flawed because of the use of inexplicit diagnostic criteria, unstated sample selection and sample size, and unsystematic data collection. Gunderson and Englund succinctly characterized the research as having two purposes: 1) descriptive, to examine psychopathology of the parents; and 2) explanatory, to formulate family traits that make a child vulnerable for developing BPD (no traits are presented that could protect a child from this outcome). The descriptive studies were summarized depending on their focus on the individual parents or the marital relationship. The mothers, according to Gunderson and Englund, were variously described as dominating, controlling, or passive and childish. Masterson's (1972) formulations suggested that mothers themselves were borderline. However, recent diagnostic studies have not supported this hypothesis (Links et al. 1988a). Fathers were seen as either passive, ineffectual, and weak or sadistic, hostile, and dominant. Gunderson and Englund summarized these studies by concluding, "Fathers of borderlines seem to share a major struggle with aggression which is manifested in either its excess, its absence or its negation." The reviewers pointed to the paucity of data characterizing the marital relationship of the parents, or the presence or absence of psychopathology in siblings.

Gunderson and Englund summarized the explanatory studies by focusing on four family traits. *Overinvolvement* of the parents with the child was characteristic of families that perceived independence as bad and promoted infantilization of the child. Masterson (1972) viewed parental inability to approve of separation and individualization as a crucial parameter of the borderline patient and described disapproval as a withdrawal of emotional supplies by mother as a child attempts to separate and individuate. Grinker et al. (1968) indicated that this family typology resists the natural process of family disintegration. *Projection* as a mode of parental functioning was the next explanatory model. Shapiro (1978) maintained that the parents project positive or negative valuations of themselves onto the child in order to maintain their own and the family's equilibrium. Rosner (1969) similarly described that the children became transferential objects for the parent's projections. Two related issues accompany this trait: 1) such parents may themselves be borderline, and 2) such families will be overinvolved with the affected child.

The third model stressed *parental neglect* as a mechanism leading to borderline psychopathology. Wolberg (1973) postulated that the degree of parental rejection accounts for the degree of child pathology, with schizophrenic patients suffering the greatest rejection, borderline patients an intermediate amount, and neurotic patients the least. Of course, such a formulation might lead to a very testable hypothesis. Meza (1970) felt continuous abuse may lead to the child's being helpless and defending himself or herself with unrelenting anger. Finally, the absence of strong mother and father figures in some families of borderline offspring was used to suggest that *role modeling*, or lack thereof, may lead to borderline psychopathology.

Gunderson and Englund distilled two major competing etiologic theories from this array of concepts. One theory suggests a hostile/dependent, overinvolved family environment; the other, a neglectful, abusive environment. Gunderson and Englund concluded that intense affects were clearly evident in the families of borderline patients; however, this conclusion needed more empirical validation. These authors raised the issue of whether these models are specific to borderline psychopathology, as similar theories had been proposed for schizophrenia and psychopathy.

Since Gunderson and Englund's review, several studies have attempted to document empirically the family environments of patients with BPD. The studies are summarized in Table 1-1.

Gunderson et al. (1980) compared the family characteristics of 12 borderline patients, 12 paranoid schizophrenic patients, and 12 hospitalized neurotic patients and tested three separate hypotheses:

1. Could blind raters predict whether a family has borderline offspring based on the family characteristics?
2. Did family traits correlate with the specific form of psychopathology found in the borderline offspring?

Table 1-1. Empirical studies of borderline family environment

Author/Year	Concept tested	Design	Sample	Measures	Concept supported
Gunderson et al. 1980	Marital difficulty; discomfort with parental roles; psychopathology in mother; psychopathology in father; alliances and splits; turmoil among siblings; nonprotective, unstable family unit	Case control	12 borderline 12 paranoid schizophrenic 12 neurotic	Items derived from literature and clinical experience; rated based on blind chart review	Both mother and father sicker and less functional (**biparental failure**); tightness of marital bond; absence of marital conflict (**neglect/loss**)
Bradley 1979	Early maternal separation	Case control	14 borderline 45 psychiatric control 23 delinquent	Separations > 3 weeks; no control for SES; not rated blindly	Early separation greater in borderline (**neglect/loss**)
Frank and Paris 1981	Parental response to dependent and independent childhood strivings	Case control	Normal, outpatients with neurosis and personality disorder, borderline (*n* not given)	Childhood Experience Scale—10 items; blind ratings	Fathers of borderline patients less approving and more disinterested (**biparental failure**); neglect > overinvolvement

Table 1-1. Empirical studies of borderline family environment—Continued

Author/Year	Concept tested	Design	Sample	Measures	Concept supported
Soloff and Millward 1983	Neurobehavioral model; separation hypothesis; family-dynamic theory	Case control	45 borderline 32 depressed 42 schizophrenic	Neurobehavioral checklist; Separation and Family Dynamic Questionnaire; Not blind	Separation (**neglect/loss**) hypothesis; Negative—conflictual relationships between patients and parents; overinvolvement in all groups more negative in borderline; father underinvolved (**biparental failure**)
Snyder et al. 1984	Describe family experience	No control group	24 male 2 female borderline	Developmental and social history	Male figure dominant in 75% of borderline patients; experienced abuse or slapping/hitting (**abuse**)
Akiskal et al. 1985	Developmental object loss; assortive parental psychopathology	Case control	100 borderline 57 schizophrenic 50 nonaffective personality 50 bipolar 40 unipolar		Borderline > unipolar on developmental loss (**neglect/loss**); parental assortive mating; borderline > unipolar (**biparental failure**)
Goldberg et al. 1985	Parental care versus overprotection	Case control	24 borderline 22 psychiatric control 10 normal	Parental Bonding Inventory (reliability and validity discussed)	Neglect/loss and overprotection interact in borderline patients

Study	Focus	Design	Sample	Measures	Findings
Zanarini et al. 1989b	Disturbed caregivers versus separations from caregivers	Case control	50 borderline 29 antisocial 26 other personality disorder (PD)	Retrospective Family Pathology Questionnaire; Retrospective Separation Experiences Questionnaire; rating blind	Verbal and sexual abuse most common in borderline patients (**abuse**); borderline > antisocial reported emotional withdrawal; Borderline > other PD prolonged separation (**neglect/loss**)
Links et al. 1988b	Evidence of separations from caregiver and abuse	Case control	88 borderline 42 borderline traits	Questions on separations, foster home placement, nonintact parental marriage, abuse by caregivers	Borderline more separation experiences, physical and sexual abuse by caregivers (**abuse and neglect/loss**)
Herman et al. 1989[a]	History of childhood trauma	Case control	21 borderline 11 borderline traits 23 schizotypal, antisocial, bipolar II	Semistructured interview on childhood histories, rated blind; Impact of Event Scale; Dissociative Experience Scale	History of trauma (**physical and sexual abuse, witness to violence**) in early childhood most common in borderline (**abuse**)

Note. SES = Socioeconomic status.
[a]Details discussed in Chapter 6.

3. Were there discriminable characteristics of borderline families compared to the other diagnostic groups?

Data on the family environment were extracted from McLean Hospital charts and then rated blindly by the authors. A list of 72 characteristics were collapsed into 11 item groups for some of the analyses based on the results of an inter-item correlation matrix. Diagnoses were made independently by two experienced psychiatrists. The authors were able to guess correctly the index diagnosis of the borderline and schizophrenic patients in 62.5% and 67% of the cases, respectively, but only 22% of the neurotic group were correctly predicted. The second hypothesis was not supported, as there was little correlation between family traits and aspects of the borderline patients' psychopathology. A discriminant function of all three groups for the 72 items showed that four items were used in the function: 1) maternal psychosis, 2) poor enforcement of rules, 3) absence of maternal overinvolvement with index patient, and 4) a tendency for one child to be seen as good and another child as bad. This function correctly classified 95.8% of all of the cases. When a discriminant function analysis was done for the 11 summary items, five components were used in the function. Four components reflected greater pathology in both parents and siblings, and one indicated that mothers of borderline patients were less likely to turn to their children as a source of gratification. Gunderson et al. (1980) concluded that the results suggested neglect as a major characteristic of the borderline family. The authors did not find evidence of overinvolvement; in fact, this was more characteristic of the neurotic and schizophrenic families. Although the mothers and fathers of borderline patients were sicker and less functional than the comparison families, Gunderson et al. (1980) found that their marriages were marked by a relative absence of overt hostility and conflict. We shall see that this finding does not appear to be in agreement with the findings of others and may reflect the uniqueness of the sample.

Bradley (1979) reported on the history of single or repeated separations from mother or caregiver for longer than 3 weeks in a sample of borderline children and adolescents compared to a group of nonborderline psychiatric patients and nonpsychiatric delinquent controls. The borderline group showed significantly more evidence of early separations (birth to 5 years) than the combined control groups. Unfortunately, the author was unable to control for socioeconomic class or welfare status, which may be potential confounders for the relationship between BPD and early separation.

To throw light on the overprotection and neglect etiologic hypotheses, Frank and Paris (1981) examined adult patients' recollections of how their parents responded to typical dependent and independent strivings. The authors found that the mothers of the borderline patients were remembered no differently from those of the comparison groups, but fathers of borderline patients were significantly more likely to be less approving or more disinterested than fathers of the two comparison groups. There was evidence to suggest that parents of borderline patients were no more critical than the parents of neurotic patients. The findings of this study seem to support the neglect hypothesis and to underline that borderline patients have experienced biparental failure.

Soloff and Millward (1983) tested three etiologic models: 1) the neurobehavioral model, which postulates a relationship between the development of adult borderline disorder and minimal brain dysfunction or early life central nervous system insult; 2) the separation hypothesis, which suggests that early life deprivation through real or threatened object loss leads to developmental arrest and resultant ego deficits; and 3) family dynamic theory, which attributes borderline development to the structure of roles assigned within the family group. Forty-five borderline patients were compared with 32 depressed and 42 schizophrenic patients regarding their developmental histories. The results did not support the neurobehavioral hypothesis, and the authors concluded that organic developmental factors were unlikely, or at least uncommon, in their sample of borderline patients. This may be partly explained by the prevalence of females in the borderline group, as male sex is more likely to be related to evidence of minimal brain dysfunction. The separation hypothesis was supported, as borderline patients had significantly fewer intact families compared to schizophrenic and depressed controls. Finally, the families of borderline patients were marked by conflictual relationships between patient and mother and patient and father compared with the families of both comparison groups. Conflict was also reported in 80% of the marriages of the parents of borderline patients, but this was also frequently found in the marriages of the parents of depressed patients. All three groups acknowledged overinvolvement between the patient and mother; however, borderline patients experienced this more negatively than the depressed and schizophrenic patients. Fathers of borderline patients were experienced as being underinvolved compared to the comparison groups. The results supported the family constellation of an overinvolved mother and underinvolved father but in the context of a marriage characterized by conflict in almost all of the families of borderline patients.

Snyder et al. (1984) reported on the family relations as recalled by 26 borderline patients. Although the study lacked comparison groups and relied mainly on subjective recollections of family interactions, the study is unique in that 24 of 26 patients were male borderline subjects. Given the difference in sex distribution from other studies, these authors found the fathers were recalled to be the dominant and central family member, and this contrasts greatly with the characterization of the father as passive and withdrawn. Sixty-two percent of the parental figures were reported to have major medical illnesses, and a majority of borderline patients recalled severe physical abuse or "moderate" corporal punishment from their parental figures. Snyder et al. (1984) called for future research to observe directly styles of interaction and to employ diagnostic control groups such as schizoid, antisocial, and schizotypal personality disorders.

Akiskal et al. (1985) examined the occurrence of developmental object loss and parental assortative mating (i.e., where both parents suffered from psychiatric disorders) in a group of 100 borderline outpatients. Thirty-seven percent of borderline patients reported childhood object loss compared to 18% of primary affective controls and 60% of personality disorder controls. The borderline probands were not different from the personality disorder controls on parental assortative mating but differed significantly from the primary affective controls. The parental unit of borderline patients most commonly suffered from alcoholism-affective disorder followed by alcoholism-sociopathy disorder. As a result, Akiskal et al. characterized the family environment as "stormy" with frequent separations and orphanage or adoption experiences. Akiskal et al.'s (1985) formulations are particularly important, as they postulate that these children may be at a "double disadvantage: they may inherit the illnesses of one or both parents, and may develop exquisite vulnerability to adult object loss as a result of the tempestuous early home environment" (p. 46).

Goldberg et al. (1985) used the Parental Binding Inventory (Parker et al. 1979) to compare the parental qualities of 24 borderline personality disorder patients to 22 patients with assorted psychiatric disorders and 10 normal controls. The borderline patients were found to perceive their parents as significantly less caring and more overprotective than both comparison groups. The findings were suggestive of a possible interaction between neglect and overprotection as antecedents to BPD.

Zanarini et al. (1989b) carried out a careful study of the childhood experiences of 50 patients with BPD, comparing them with 29 patients with antisocial personality disorder and 26 patients with dysthymic disorder plus other types of Axis II disorders. The childhood experiences were assessed by raters blind to all diagnostic information about a subject. The assessment included inquiry about verbal, physical, and sexual abuse perpetrated by the patients' full-time caregivers or evidence of physical neglect, emotional withdrawal, or inconsistent treatment by their caregivers. A significantly higher percentage of borderline patients reported being verbally and sexually abused before the age of 18 than the other comparison groups; however, the reporting of physical abuse did not differentiate the groups. Eighty percent of the borderline patients reported some type of abuse at the hands of their full-time caregivers. Borderline probands were differentiated from antisocial controls by a history of having a caregiver withdraw from them emotionally, whereas the incidence of early childhood separations differentiated borderline probands from the dysthymic disorder controls. Again, this study found group differences on socioeconomic class and sex distribution but did not examine for the confounding effects of these variables.

Our own study (Links et al. 1988b) compared a group of 88 borderline inpatients defined by the Diagnostic Interview for Border-lines (Gunderson et al. 1981) with a comparison group of 42 in-patients with personality disorder features but not meeting criteria for BPD. The borderline patients were significantly more likely to have experienced a separation from mother for more than 3 months, more likely to have been placed in a foster home, and more likely to have come from a home with a nonintact marriage than the comparison group. The borderline probands also reported being abused physically and sexually by their caregivers more often than the comparison group. Although this study used a conservative comparison group of patients who shared traits of BPD, the borderline patients were more likely to report having suffered separation/loss and abuse in childhood.

The frequent reporting of sexual abuse in the backgrounds of borderline patients has recently been confirmed by other authors. Bryer et al. (1987) surveyed 68 female inpatients and found that BPD was the most frequent Axis II diagnosis among the 29 inpatients who had experienced early sexual abuse (occurring before age 16). Of the 14 subjects with BPD, 12 had experienced early sexual abuse. Herman et al. (1989) has also found abuse histories to be significantly related to the BPD diagnosis. This study will be reviewed in greater detail in Chapter 6 when we examine possible etiologic mechanisms leading to BPD. Two of the reports in this volume, by Ogata et al. (Chapter 5) and Stone (Chapter 8), provide further confirmation of the relationship between abuse and BPD.

DISCUSSION

Our review of the literature on the impact of the family environment on the development of BPD indicates a shift away from concern for a specific phase of development, for example, the separation-individuation phase. The family environment of borderline patients appears to expose these offspring to chronic stress rather than to episodic stress or a single traumatic event. Three etiologic mechanisms were suggested from the literature, and each of these will be discussed.

Early Separation and Loss Experience

At least eight of the authors reviewed found empirical evidence supporting the concept of neglect or deprivation because of early separation from, or loss of, a primary caregiver (Akiskal et al. 1985; Bradley 1979; Frank and Paris 1981; Goldberg et al. 1985; Gunderson et al. 1980; Links et al. 1988b; Soloff and Millward 1983; Zanarini et al. 1989b). Of course, a similar etiologic connection has proposed that early object loss predisposes to depressive disorder, and, although different reviewers have come to varying conclusions about the strength and significance of this association, Lloyd (1980) concluded that parental bereavement during childhood increases the risk of depression in adulthood by a factor of 2 to 3. Rutter (1983) noted that few studies have examined other forms of loss in early childhood, few have provided data on the family processes surrounding the loss, and few have examined the interactive effects of early loss in conjunction with later loss. Brown and Harris (1978) suggested that past loss influences the symptom pattern of depression, with loss by death predisposing to psychotic depression and loss by separation predisposing to neurotic depression. Our own studies suggested that the vast majority of nonintact marriages of parents of borderline patients were due to marital separation, whereas those in the comparison group were more likely due to death of a parent (Links et al. 1988b). The protective role of the remaining parent after loss was suggested by Birtchnell (1980), and it may be the inadequacy of the remaining parent that is an important aspect leading to borderline psychopathology.

Different mechanisms have been proposed to explain the connection between early loss and the predisposition to psychiatric disorder. Current theories suggest that the association of early loss to psychopathology is far too simplistic and that future research will study how childhood attachments lead to internal mental constructions that predict adult attachments and the response of adults to real or threatened object loss. Davis and Akiskal (1986) hypothesized that for some borderline patients,

> early separation and loss may permanently affect the neural pathways
> of biogenic amines and endorphins that underlie the reinforcement

mechanisms. A disruption of such reinforcement mechanisms is an appealing etiology for much of the self-destructive and socially inept behaviours that characterize borderline patients. (p. 690)

Thus, early parental loss, probably due to separation rather than death, could predispose a child to borderline psychopathology. The magnitude of this impairment may be partly determined by the protection conferred on the child by the remaining parent.

Sexual and Physical Abuse in Early Childhood

The occurrence of sexual and physical child abuse as part of the causal chain of events in the development of BPD has been supported by several recent studies (Bryer et al. 1987; Herman et al. 1989; Links et al. 1988b; Ogata et al., Chapter 5; Stone, Chapter 8, this volume; Zanarini et al. 1989b).

Evidence for exposure to prolonged and varied abuse was supported by the work of Herman et al. (1989) and Bryer et al. (1987). Bryer et al. (1987) examined the rates of childhood abuse in a sample of 68 female inpatients consecutively admitted to a private psychiatric hospital. They found that subjects who had experienced both physical and sexual abuse had higher mean symptom scores than subjects who experienced only one type of abuse or subjects who had not been abused at all. In addition, borderline symptoms as measured by the Millon Clinical Multiaxial Inventory (Millon 1983) significantly differentiated between the three levels of childhood abuse.

Soloff and Millward (1983) found that overinvolvement with mother was present in all patient groups, but the unique aspect of the borderline patient's environment was the fact that this overinvolvement was perceived negatively by the patient. Goldberg et al. (1985) suggested an interaction between evidence of less caring and over-protectiveness in the parents of borderline patients. Hostile and conflictual relationships appear to be a characteristic of the borderline family environment as supported by Soloff and Millward (1983) and by the findings of Snyder et al. (1984). This raises the hypothesis that overinvolvement between patient and parent may not be unique to the borderline family, but the interaction of the overinvolvement with an expression of hostility may create the characteristic environment. We have been struck by the fact that this hostility appears to indicate a highly malevolent attitude of the parent toward the child. We speculate that the interaction of overinvolvement plus this malevolent attitude is particularly characteristic of the childhood environment of the borderline patient. The polarities of overinvolvement and malevolence would be characterized by parents who persistently physically or sexually abused their children from an early age.

In summary, borderline personality disorder appears to stem at least in part from the early and prolonged effects of physical and sexual abuse on the child's developing personality. The mechanisms by which these traumata act require further examination but may be a result of the interaction between parental overinvolvement and malevolence.

Biparental Failure

At least four of the authors reviewed found that both mothers and fathers showed significant impairment and a failure to carry out their parental functions (Akiskal et al. 1985; Frank and Paris 1981; Gunderson et al. 1980; Soloff and Millward 1983). Frank and Paris (1981) spoke of the occurrence of biparental failure that appeared to be reflected by their findings on the father's role in the development of borderline psychopathology. However, the characterization of father as underinvolved may be related to the sex of the identified proband. For example, Snyder et al. (1984) found in their study of male borderline patients that the father was the dominant figure in the family. This evidence suggests that the parental roles may vary depending on the sex of the affected offspring. Akiskal et al. (1985) also noted that assortive mating was commonly found in the parents of borderline patients, and whether this reflected a genetic or environmental risk, it seemed to be characteristic of the borderline patient's family in comparison to patients with affective disorder.

Even putting the role of genetic factors aside, evidence of significant impairment in the patient's parents can have major effects on the exposed offspring. Richters and Weintraub (in press) reviewed the diathesis stress model employed in high-risk studies to explain the etiology of schizophrenia. They cautioned that early maladjustment in the offspring of a schizophrenic parent is not necessarily synonymous with vulnerability to the disorder, and this early maladjustment can be reflective of acquired rather than inherited defects. Rutter and Quinton (1984) outlined several causal explanations for the association between parental psychopathology and offspring maladjustment. Apart from genetic transmission, the parents' symptoms may have a direct impact on the child's learning and development, the parents' psychopathology may interfere with the parents' functioning, or the parents' psychopathology may lead to marital discord. The parents of borderline patients often evidence severe psychopathology themselves (Links et al. 1988a; Ogata et al., Chapter 5; Zanarini et al., Chapter 4, this volume), and the environmental impact of this psychopathology on the offspring may be of great etiologic significance and is the focus of several of the chapters of this volume.

In summary, prior investigations of the family environments of patients with BPD support a relationship between BPD and families characterized by early loss and separation, neglect and abuse, and biparental failure. Although these areas of family dysfunction are hypothesized as causal or contributing agents in a number of psychiatric disorders, evidence would suggest that these family characteristics are more strongly associated with BPD than with schizophrenia, bipolar disorder, or neurotic disorders. Paradoxically, parental overinvolvement has also been associated with BPD as well as with a number of other disorders. In contrast to other patient groups, however, borderline patients tend to view the parental overinvolvement as negative. It may be that it is the parental overinvolvement in combination with neglect and abuse that proves toxic for borderline patients.

Many questions arise from these findings concerning the ways in which family characteristics relate to BPD. It is likely that there are multiple causal pathways for borderline disorder, and the nature and extent of the contribution of family environment remains to be determined. Research methodologies have been developed to investigate the contributions of family characteristics to the onset and course of several other psychiatric disorders, and, in particular, the relationship between family variables and schizophrenia has been explored in depth. These methodologies may be useful in advancing knowledge regarding family contributions to borderline disorder.

RESEARCH METHODOLOGIES

In order to demonstrate meaningfully the etiological contributions of family environment to BPD, it will be necessary to satisfy, at least in part, the scientific criteria for establishing causality. As put forward by Hill in 1965 and expanded by the Department of Clinical Epidemiology and Biostatistics at McMaster University (1981), these criteria are as follows:

- A strong association exists between the putative causal factor and disorder.
- Consistency of the association is demonstrated across studies.
- Correct temporal relationship, that is, the causal factor precedes disorder in time.
- A dose-response relationship, or an increased risk of disease with an increase in exposure to the putative cause.
- The association makes epidemiological sense, that is, it agrees with the current understanding of the distributions of causes and outcomes.

- The association makes biological sense, that is, it agrees with current understanding of the biology of the problem.
- The association is specific, that is, limited to a specific cause and effect.
- The association is analogous to a previously proven causal relationship.

A further criterion might be added, that is, the elimination of the causal factor leads to decreased incidence of the disorder.

One quick glance at these criteria demonstrates the distance to be travelled in establishing a strong causal relationship between family environment and BPD. A shift toward clinical surveys and case control studies and away from reliance on the reporting of individual clinical cases allows for better demonstration of the strength of the association between family factors and borderline disorder and the consistency of these findings across studies. Such studies do not, however, address issues such as temporality and dose-response relationship. In addition, cross-sectional and retrospective studies are subject to a number of forms of bias, including selective recall, measurement bias, and confounding, which may lead to a distorted perspective on the relationship between familial characteristics and BPD. For example, the relationship between prior sexual abuse and borderline disorder that has been demonstrated in several studies may be explained by a third factor, female gender, which is associated with both the occurrence of sexual abuse and the diagnosis of BPD.

Research into etiology would benefit most from prospective studies that can examine the temporal relationship between putative variables and the incidence of the outcome of interest. Given the low incidence of BPD in the general population, however, prospective population studies are not likely to be feasible. On the other hand, prospective study of high-risk individuals without borderline disorder, or newly diagnosed borderline patients identified through clinic samples, might be more fruitful. The emphasis here must be on accurate identification of risk variables. Prospective studies will need to differentiate between investigation of disorder-initiating and disorder-promoting factors. Of course, both kinds of variables are important in understanding the onset and course of BPD.

Longitudinal studies in conjunction with well-conducted treatment outcome studies can contribute to an understanding of etiological and disorder-promoting factors if two conditions are satisfied. In the first case, risk factors should predict new cases or poor prognosis of the disorder. In the second, interventions that lead to a decrease in the patients' exposure to a suspected contributing agent (such as familial abuse) should lead to an associated decrease in the disorder. Retrospective cohort studies that compare borderline cases to non-cases on familial exposures of interest and prospective cohort studies comparing high-risk subjects (new cases and noncases) with those without suspected contributing characteristics will be fruitful only insofar as the measurements of disorder and exposure are sound.

Recently, progress has been made in the development and application of well-defined, reliable diagnostic criteria to establish BPD (Frances et al. 1984; Gunderson and Zanarini 1987; Hurt et al. 1984; Zanarini et al. 1989a). Similarly, reliable diagnostic procedures exist for selecting comparison groups of patients with other psychiatric disorders. On the other hand, the measurement of family conditions that may lead to the initiation or promotion of borderline disorder has been inconsistent and questionable in terms of satisfying psychometric properties of reliability and validity. Research into family influences on schizophrenia has resulted in advancements in the measurement of family characteristics that may be well suited for investigations of BPD. In particular, measures of family interactions, especially measures of family emotional climate, can be directly measured through assessment of family member expressed emotion (EE) toward the subject, replacing reliance on the subject's recollections of the family environment. The construct of expressed emotion was developed from the study of schizophrenia patients, but this construct may have application to the study of family environment and borderline disorder.

Expressed Emotion

Expressed emotion is the term used to refer to the overall index of a relative's emotional relationship with a disordered family member. The index is composed of ratings of three components of relatives' expressed attitudes and feelings about the patient: 1) number of critical comments made about the patient, 2) hostility, and 3) emotional overinvolvement. The ratings are based on both the content of relatives' statements and the vocal tone displayed (Leff and Vaughn 1985; Magana et al. 1986).

The Camberwell Family Interview (CFI) (Brown and Rutter 1966) is the instrument first developed to measure EE, and it has good reliability and validity characteristics. Family high EE status as measured on the CFI has been associated with a high risk for relapse at both 9 months and 2 years after hospital discharge (Brown et al. 1972; Leff and Vaughn 1981). In addition, schizophrenic patients in those families who have had EE reduced through social interventions experience decreased relapse in comparison with high EE control families (Hogarty et al. 1986; Leff et al. 1985). Although the contributions of the CFI as a measure of family member EE have been substantial, the method of assessment is laborious, taking 1½ to 2 hours to administer and 3 to 4 or more hours to rate. In addition, extensive training is required to prepare assessors.

An alternative method for evaluating family member EE is a derivation of the Five Minute Speech Sample (FMSS) developed by Gottschalk and Gleser (1969) and adapted to assessment of EE by Magana and colleagues (1986). In this assessment procedure, key relatives are prompted to speak, uninterrupted, for 5 minutes, stating what kind of a person the ill relative is and how the respondent gets along with him or her. The speech sample is recorded and then rated directly from the audiotape by trained raters using an established, manual-based rating procedure. Although the raters must be trained in the procedure, the examiners follow a simple set of instructions and need not be trained in order to elicit the speech sample.

There is a high degree of correspondence between the CFI and FMSS, although the FMSS may rate a small number of family members as low EE when they are judged high EE on the CFI (Magana et al. 1986). A conservative approach, then, would be to use the FMSS as a screening instrument and to use the CFI only on those families rated low EE on the FMSS. On the other hand, although the CFI was the first measure of EE, there is little to suggest that it is the gold standard for assessment of EE. In comparison with the CFI, the FMSS derives EE ratings that are more evenly distributed between high and low EE (M. Goldstein, November 1987, personal communication).

Studies investigating and comparing the predictive validity of the two measures will contribute data toward answering the "gold standard" question. In the meantime, there is little question that the FMSS offers useful data on the EE status of family members, and it is quick and inexpensive to administer. It provides ratings of the overall relationship (positive, negative, or neutral) of the family member to the patient and provides ratings of the family member criticism/hostility and emotional overinvolvement toward the patient (Magana et al. 1986). The FMSS is well accepted by family members. It is proposed that use of this measure in borderline studies would lend needed rigor to the assessment of the family characteristics of borderline patients and would tap several dimensions of family relationships previously indicated as important to understanding the course and possibly the onset of the disorder. In particular, the coexistence of parental overinvolvement and negative relationship may be relevant for understanding BPD. In addition, because EE can be measured independently for each family member, it could provide a systematic means of describing various configurations of biparental failure, which could then be compared with uniparental failure in terms of its relationship to borderline disorder. The FMSS would allow one to test the hypothesis that parental overinvolvement in the face of criticism and abuse is most toxic for borderline patients. In addition, the FMSS could be used in studies of family interventions with relatives of borderline patients to evaluate whether changes in the EE status of relatives lead to improvement for the patient.

SUMMARY

Prior research supports an association between BPD and biparental failure, parental overinvolvement, separation, neglect, and abuse. It is difficult, given the current state of knowledge, to determine whether these factors contribute primarily to the onset of the disorder or to the course and outcome of the disorder. In addition, it is not yet clear which constellations or clusters of negative family characteristics, if any, best differentiate BPD from other psychiatric disorders. Studies of the predictive validity of biparental failure, parental overinvolvement, criticism, and negative relationship to the subject may add to knowledge regarding family contributions to BPD. These particular family characteristics might best be investigated by employing retrospective and prospective cohort studies designed specifically to address the relationship of these family characteristics to either onset of the disorder (following young, high-risk, nonborderline subjects) or the course of the disorder (following relatively new cases of disorder with and without the family risk characteristics). The FMSS is proposed as an assessment procedure that would be feasible in such studies and that provides a more rigorous measure of important family characteristics than has been possible in studies of family contributions to BPD.

REFERENCES

Adler G: Borderline Psychopathology and Its Treatment. New York, Jason Aronson, 1985

Akiskal HS, Chen ES, Davis GC, et al: Borderline: an adjective in search of a noun. J Clin Psychiatry 46:41–48, 1985

American Psychiatric Association: Diagnostic and Statistical Manual of Mental Disorders, 3rd Edition, Revised. Washington, DC, American Psychiatric Association, 1987

Birtchnell J: Women whose mothers died in childhood: an outcome study. Psychol Med 10:669–713, 1980

Bradley SJ: Relation of early maternal separation to borderline personality in children and adolescents: a pilot study. Am J Psychiatry 136:424–426, 1979

Brown FW, Rutter ML: The measurement of family activities and relationships. Human Relations 19:241–263, 1966

Brown GW, Harris T: Social Origins of Depression: A Study of Psychiatric Disorder in Women. New York, Free Press, 1978

Brown GW, Birley JT, Wing JK: Influence of family life on the course of schizophrenic disorders: a replication. Br J Psychiatry 121:241–258, 1972

Bryer JB, Nelson BA, Miller JB, et al: Childhood sexual and physical abuse as factors in adult psychiatric illness. Am J Psychiatry 144:1426–1430, 1987

Davis GC, Akiskal HS: Descriptive, biological, and theoretical aspects of borderline personality disorder. Hosp Community Psychiatry 37:685–692, 1986

Department of Clinical Epidemiology and Biostatistics, McMaster University: How to read clinical journals: IV. To determine etiology or causation. CMA Journal 124:985–990, 1981

Frances A, Clarkin J, Gilmore M, et al: Reliability of criteria for borderline personality disorder: a comparison of DSM-III and the diagnostic interview for borderline patients. Am J Psychiatry 141:1080–1084, 1984

Frank H, Paris J: Recollections of family experience in borderline patients. Arch Gen Psychiatry 38:1031–1034, 1981

Goldberg RL, Mann LS, Wisc TN, et al: Parental qualities as perceived by BPDs. Hillside J Clin Psychiatry 7:134–140, 1985

Gottschalk LA, Gleser GO: The Measurement of Psychological States Through Analysis of Verbal Behavior. Berkeley, CA, University of California Press, 1969

Grinker R, Werble B, Drye R: The Borderline Syndrome. New York, Basic Books, 1968

Gunderson J, Englund D: Characterizing the families of borderlines. Psychiatr Clin North Am 4:159–168, 1981

Gunderson JG, Zanarini MC: Current overview of the borderline diagnosis. J Clin Psychiatry 48:5–14, 1987

Gunderson JG, Kerr J, Englund DW: The families of borderlines: a comparative study. Arch Gen Psychiatry 37:27–33, 1980

Gunderson JG, Kolb JE, Austin V: The diagnostic interview for borderline patients. Am J Psychiatry 138:896–903, 1981

Herman JL, Perry JC, van der Kolk BA: Childhood trauma in borderline personality disorder. Am J Psychiatry 146:490–495, 1989

Hill AB: The environment and disease: association or causation? Proceedings of the Royal Society of Medicine (London) 58:295–300, 1965

Hogarty GE, Anderson CM, Reiss DJ, et al: Family psychoeducation, social skills training and maintenance chemotherapy in the aftercare treatment of schizophrenia. Arch Gen Psychiatry 43:633–642, 1986

Hurt SW, Hyler S, Frances A, et al: Assessing borderline personality disorder with self-report, clinical interview or semistructured interview. Am J Psychiatry 141:1228–1231, 1984

Kernberg OF: Severe Personality Disorders. Psychotherapeutic Strategies. New Haven, CT, Yale University Press, 1984

Leff JP, Vaughn CE: The role of maintenance therapy and relatives' expressed emotion in relapse of schizophrenia: a two-year followup. Br J Psychiatry 139:102–104, 1981

Leff JP, Vaughn C (eds): Expressed Emotion in Families. Its Significance and Mental Illness. New York, Guilford, 1985

Leff JP, Kuipers L, Berkowitz R, et al: A controlled trial of social intervention in the families of schizophrenic patients: two-year followup. Br J Psychiatry 146:594–600, 1985

Links PS, Steiner M, Huxley G: The occurrence of borderline personality disorder in the families of borderline patients. J Pers Disord 2:14–20, 1988a

Links PS, Steiner M, Offord DR, et al: Characteristics of borderline personality disorder: a Canadian study. Can J Psychiatry 33:336–340, 1988b

Lloyd C: Life events and depressive disorder reviewed: I. Events as predisposing factors. Arch Gen Psychiatry 37:529–535, 1980

Magana A, Goldstein M, Karno M, et al: A brief method for assessing expressed emotion in relatives of psychiatric patients. Psychiatry Res 17:203–212, 1986

Mahler MS: A study of the separation-individuation process and its possible application to borderline phenomena in the psychoanalytic situation. Psychoanal Study Child 26:403–424, 1971

Masterson JF: Treatment of the Borderline Adolescent: A Developmental Approach. New York, Wiley-Interscience, 1972

Meza C: El Colerico. Mexico City, Mortz, 1970

Millon T: Millon Clinical Multiaxial Inventory Manual, 3rd Edition. Minneapolis, MN, National Computer Systems, 1983

Parker G, Tapling H, Brown LB: A parental bonding instrument. Br J Med Psychol 52:1–10, 1979

Richters J, Weintraub S: Beyond diathesis: towards an understanding of high risk environments in risk and protective factors, in The Development of Psychopathology. Edited by Rolf JE, Masten A, Cicchetti D, et al. New York, Cambridge University Press (in press)

Rosner S: Problems of working through with borderline patients. Psychotherapy 6:43–45, 1969

Rutter M: Stress, coping and development: some issues and some questions, in Stress, Coping and Development in Children. Edited by Garmazy N, Rutter M. New York, McGraw-Hill, 1983, pp 1–41

Rutter M, Quinton D: Parental psychiatric disorder: effects on children. Psychol Med 14:853–880, 1984

Shapiro ER: The psychodynamics and developmental psychology of the borderline patient: a review of the literature. Am J Psychiatry 135:1305–1315, 1978

Snyder S, Pitts WM, Goodpaster WA, et al: Family structure as recalled by borderline patients. Psychopathology 17:90–97, 1984

Soloff PH, Millward JW: Developmental histories of borderline patients. Compr Psychiatry 24:547–588, 1983

Stone MH: Borderline syndrome: a consideration of subtypes and an overview: directions for research. Psychiatr Clin North Am 4:3–24, 1981

Wolberg A: The Borderline Patient. New York, Intercontinental Medical Book Corporation, 1973

Zanarini MC, Gunderson JG, Frankenburg FR, et al: Revised Diagnostic Interview for Borderlines: discriminating borderline personality disorder from other Axis II disorders. Journal of Personality Disorders 3:10–18, 1989a

Zanarini MC, Gunderson JG, Mario MS, et al: Childhood experiences of borderline patients. Compr Psychiatry 30:18–25, 1989b

Chapter 2

Interpersonal Disorder in Borderline Patients

Barry M. Segal, M.B., B.Ch.

Chapter 2

Interpersonal Disorder in Borderline Patients

This chapter is a review of some major dynamic theories of the borderline disorder. The theories will be classified according to their models of psychopathology, and their approaches to treatment and etiology will be compared. These theories have been derived from clinical experience and serve as models for clinical work and as frameworks for research. They remain central to our conceptualization of borderline patients due to the limitations of empirical research in this area. In this book, the theories serve as points of reference for comparison to the empirical research.

Dynamic approaches to individual psychotherapy with borderline patients are related by their emphasis on interpersonal aspects. Many borderline symptoms are seen as arising primarily within the context of a relationship, where the involvement of another person is the arena in which an essential component of the patient's psychopathology emerges. This pathology lies in the patient's reduced capacity to function as an independent self and to relate to others realistically. The theories dealing with this can be visualized on a spectrum between object-relations theory on one hand and self psychology on the other. There are some important differences between these theories, which lead to important differences in the approach to psychotherapy that evolves (Waldinger 1987).

Object-relations approaches focus on the experience and perception of self and others. They postulate that profound distortions of objects occur in these patients, due to unconscious forces such as strivings, defenses, and, in particular, conflict. Self-psychology approaches shift the emphasis to the other sphere in the "figure-ground" relationship of self and others and conceptualize the person as having no coherent sense of self as a separate, whole being, requiring the

The author wishes to thank Heather Munroe Blum, David Dawson, Elsa Marziali, and Norma Estee.

involvement of another person to compensate somehow for the deficit.

We will consider some important dynamic theorists in relation to these issues and compare their ideas to those of Dawson (Dawson 1988), which we are testing in our study (Munroe Blum et al. 1987–1989, 1990–1992). These theorists can be loosely placed along a spectrum between object relations and self psychology as shown in Figure 2-1.

The psychopathological constructs will be compared on the degree to which they emphasize unconscious conflicts as opposed to deficits in the self. The constructs will also be compared on the degree to which they emphasize the external object, as opposed to the self and object in relation to the self. The view that the object exists only in relation to the self implies a stage of development that precedes the individuation process.

The therapeutic models will be compared on the degree to which they emphasize interpretations, as opposed to actual experience the patient has with the therapist that is somewhat independent of understanding and insight. The latter are referred to in this chapter

OBJECT RELATIONS	SELF PSYCHOLOGY

KERNBERG — MASTERSON — GUNDERSON — ADLER/BUIE — DAWSON

Focus on — self and object	Focus on — self and self-object
— distortions of external object	— deficit in the self
	— object as part of self
— unconscious striving, defenses + conflict	
	— context level of therapy (the process of therapy, e.g., holding environment)
— content level of therapy (interpretation, confrontation)	

Figure 2-1. Theorists are arranged along a spectrum between object relations and self psychology. Psychopathological constructs, treatment approaches, and etiological theories vary across spectrum. At left, theories are based on conflict; at right, they are based on deficit in the self. At left, they emphasize interpretations; at right, they stress the experience of the therapeutic relationship.

as being process oriented. The therapeutic models will be covered in brief outline only.

The etiological models will be compared according to their emphasis on constitutional factors as opposed to environmental factors. The environmental factors will be compared according to their emphasis on the failure of the environment to meet physical needs as opposed to empathic needs.

MAJOR DYNAMIC THEORISTS

Kernberg

Kernberg defines borderline patients as having what he describes as borderline personality organization (Kernberg 1967). This is centered on the idea that their interactions reflect primitive object relationships, which result from a failure in the integration of good and bad self and object images. Defenses arise to protect the good self, the good object image, and the good external object. These defenses are splitting, primitive idealization, and early forms of projection, especially projective identification.

The recommended treatment is a modified analysis focusing on elaborating the negative transference from an early stage (Kernberg 1968). Confronting and interpreting defenses as well as structuring the therapeutic situation are also included. This view of conflicts between split objects includes a significant focus on the distortions of the external object that emerge in the negative transference. Without interpretation, Kernberg believes that ongoing reinternalizing of bad projections prevents progress. It is this emphasis on a distorted external object that locates Kernberg at one end of the spectrum; at the other end, the focus is on the self and the self objects.

Inherited tendencies have been put forward by Kernberg as pathogenic in producing the characteristic intrapsychic structure of the borderline patient. These tendencies manifest as excessive rage and anxiety responses, and as excessive oral aggression.

Kernberg accepts the possibility that environmental failure in infancy can lead to the syndrome in the absence of the inherited tendency. His concept of severe early frustration (Kernberg 1967) seems to imply an environment that fails to meet the basic physical needs of the infant. This suggests an infant who is hungry, cold, attacked, or abandoned, and a failure of the mother or caregiver to provide the first level of adequate care, such as feeding and protection from injury. Kernberg does accept the etiological role of the mother's failure to support individuation.

Masterson

The ideas of Masterson show an increased focus on the issues of the self through the importance given to Mahler's writings on separation-individuation (Masterson and Rinsley 1975). Borderline patients are seen as being fixated in a substage of the separation-individuation process, probably at the phase of rapprochement (Mahler and La-Perriere 1965). In this stage, the child is in an ambivalent state between need for the mother and individuality. Fixation occurs due to the mother's withholding of support for individuation. This conflict leads to feelings of abandonment depression, which, Masterson states, constitute one diagnostic hallmark of the borderline syndrome. The other diagnostic hallmark is narcissistic oral fixation, which shifts the emphasis of this theory to other areas such as defenses, object splitting, and ego structure.

The psychotherapy of these patients occurs in three phases (Masterson 1973):

1. In the first phase, the fear of reexperiencing abandonment is defended against with acting out. This serves to test the therapist, who must control acting out very directly to make the behaviors ego-dystonic.
2. When this is achieved, abandonment depression emerges, and the patient becomes able to work through the "rage and depression at the abandonment and complete the separation process" (Masterson 1973, p. 261). Interpretations are crucial in this stage.
3. The final phase deals with separation.

Thus, Masterson's approach retains the idea of a conflict at the center of the pathology. The resolution of conflicts with the aid of interpretations is the predominant component of the treatment.

Masterson's approach to etiology emphasizes the idea that the mother fails to provide adequate support for individuation. This failure occurs later in the child's development than severe early frustration, implying that the basic physical needs were met. The infant is rewarded only for the role of infant, being dependent and needy, and in this role the child will be rewarded with good basic care including feeding, holding, warmth, and protection. However, there is a failure of a higher order of care: The parent fails to provide emotional back-up to the child's emerging separateness as it appears in the child's explorations away from the mother. Without this support, the infant becomes fixated in the rapprochement stage as described. This lack of support may range from active discouragement of separateness to emotional withdrawal in response to indications of separation-individuation.

Masterson visualizes a family background in which the infant's mother has a borderline personality disorder (Masterson 1972). This results from her own abandonment depression, which she deals with by clinging to her child. Masterson describes the family as matriarchal, with the father in a distant, passive, or nonexistent role. The father does not provide an adequate masculine figure and is inadequate in the role of second-love object. In fact, he also has a borderline syndrome, and his failure to support the mother makes her symbiotic need stronger.

Gunderson

Gunderson's approach is essentially interpersonal. He states that the major characteristics of patients with borderline personality disorder can be understood as reactive to the nature of their major interpersonal relationships (Gunderson 1984). Three levels of interaction are described:

1. The object is experienced as supportive, and the response is dysphoria, depression, and masochism, due to the patients' fears of being let down in their hopes for closeness.
2. When the major figure is experienced as frustrating, the response is anger, devaluation, and manipulation. These serve to deny separation anxiety, although they also prevent loss by dramatizing need, as in suicide attempts.
3. When the major figure is experienced as absent, the response is psychosis and panic.

Gunderson links his outline to both sides of the spectrum, including themes from Kernberg, Masterson, and Adler and Buie. The theory is balanced between these points, and the approach is basically phenomenological.

Gunderson accepts the role of supportive psychotherapy for these cases and feels that intensive therapy should be chosen only when circumstances are very suitable. He describes four stages (Gunderson 1984), which resemble Masterson's three stages: 1) A struggle around boundaries—important interventions are felt to be consistent interpretations of the patient's demands for indications of love, and active clarification of anger; 2) negativity and control, in which anger is directed at the therapist, whose steadfast nonretaliatory stance allows for the development of improved self boundaries and tolerance of frustration; 3) separation and identity; and 4) termination, initiative, and letting go.

Thus, Gunderson deals with both the distortions and the defenses around the object as well as the self and the self objects. In his approach, he advocates interpretation and confrontation, especially of negative transferences, as well as validation of the patient's new feelings and perceptions.

Etiologic aspects have been addressed by Gunderson and colleagues. In their review of the literature on characterizing the families of borderline patients, Gunderson and Englund (1981) organized the papers into descriptive and dynamic approaches. Descriptive approaches give accounts of mother, father, marital relationship, and siblings. Dynamic approaches look at the process of family life and define four major types of processes that may occur in these families: 1) overinvolvement, 2) projection, 3) neglect, and 4) role modeling. Neglect was the typical dynamic pattern of the borderline parents in the comparative study performed by Gunderson et al. (1980). This supports the perspective of the other studies in the review that these patients experience early abuse, neglect, and poor nurturance from their parents. This results from hostile-dependent elements in the parents, expressed as various forms of splits in family life. The dominant theme is the attribution by the parents of unrealistic or partly realistic characteristics to their children, which is a replication of the parents' experience in their own childhood.

Gunderson departs from Masterson's ideas in several ways. He stresses that not just borderline pathology but various forms of psychopathology in the parents may be involved and that the environmental failure is not phase specific but plays an ongoing role throughout multiple phases of development, beginning in the symbiotic phase.

Adler and Buie

Adler and Buie (1979) describe two forms of experience that are needed for the development of the self: 1) the narcissistic needs related to personal value and 2) the more primary need for holding. Holding was described by Winnicott (1960) as reducing the fear of annihilation through reliable care that protects and is responsive to growth and development. Fear of annihilation is described as the "loss of the self through psychological disintegration as a consequence of being abandoned" (Buie and Adler 1982, p. 59). The holding object functions as the soothing part of the self and is named the "holding self-object." In health, an internalized holding self-object develops and takes over the soothing role leading to the fundamental integration of the self. In borderline patients, the internalized holding self-object is absent because of inadequate holding in infancy. Thus, in this approach the focus is on the deficit in the self and on the object as part of the self.

Adler and Buie's approach to treatment has as its first aim the therapist's becoming a holding self-object (Adler 1979). The patient's rage, envy, and fear of destruction of the self object must be addressed. Adler and Buie advocate confrontation and interpretation, but the essence of their approach is provision of a real holding environment in which they are very available to their patients. When the first aim is achieved, a second phase begins which deals with the resolution of the idealizations of the holding self-object. The third phase is super-ego maturation and formation of sustaining introjections.

Adler and Buie describe borderline patients as having no internalized holding self-object. This causes a sense of aloneness, which is associated with tenuous object constancy and deficient capacity to evoke the memory of the mother in her absence. These lead to the activation of rage as a predominant affect.

A failure to provide adequate care to the infant is felt to lead to borderline patients having no internalized holding self-object (Adler and Buie 1979). The authors point to the work of Winnicott (1960), who describes the first stage of adequate care as the provision of a holding environment. In creating this environment, the mother meets physiological needs and is reliable and nonmechanical. Thus, care has an alive responsiveness achieved through the mother's empathic understanding of the infant's feelings and needs. Essential to this is the mother's capacity to respond to the child's communication signals in a process of attuning care in a unique way, which fosters the child's sense of personal existence. The focus is on the mother and child; the father's role is recognized as dealing with the environment for the mother. Failure of the holding environment occurs when physiological or empathic needs are not met. Examples range from unavoidable separation to angry attacks on the child. Winnicott (1960) suggests that these deficiencies may result from mental ill-health in the mother.

DAWSON

The model we are testing is based on relationship management as described by Dawson (1988). This approach bridges self psychology and interpersonal theory. The interpersonal component deals with the idea that context and process in interactions determine the content level of communications and produce symptoms. The self-psychology component deals with the nature of the self system that emerges in the interpersonal context. In borderline patients, the self system is overly context bound. This results from lack of resolution of self-attribute polarities, such as good as opposed to bad, or healthy as opposed to sick. Relationships become a confrontation of polarities—

for example, the good therapist leads to the bad patient, who becomes incompetent, sick, helpless, or suicidal.

The approach to therapy is for the therapist to avoid the distortions of role imposed by the patient. This is done by attempting to adopt a neutral stance, which may be thought of as a position balanced between the polarities of the self attributes. Thus, opposing role states are minimized in the patient. In this context, the patient's behavior becomes less extreme, and his or her self system is strengthened. Neither interpretations nor very supportive availability are used, as these are seen as being role positions (i.e., wise or good).

A major criticism of relationship management may be that it deals with a stage that precedes true psychotherapy. Thus, it may be equivalent to the testing phase of Masterson or the boundaries phase of Gunderson. On the other hand, it could produce a corrective experience possibly because the therapist is a steady and calm presence performing a stabilizing function for the patient.

Thus, this is an approach with the entire focus on process, where the therapist avoids the patient's deviant interpersonal schema. The therapist is an anchored point between the extremes of role relationships, enabling the patient to adopt a more integrated position. The focus on the self and on the therapist in relation to the self, and exclusive focus on process, place this approach on the right of the spectrum.

In the study by Dawson (1988), we are told that an important developmental task of childhood and adolescence is the resolution of self-attribute polarities. Borderline patients have failed to integrate these extremes and, thus, have unstable self systems. As a result, they adopt extreme role positions in interpersonal relationships in reaction to the role position of others. The cause of the lack of integration is not explained, but etiological aspects can be inferred from the therapeutic approach.

In this approach, the therapist should adopt a role position representing a midpoint between the polarities of the self attributes. This will reduce the patient's tendency toward reactive role extremes. The therapist's role position should be steady and neutral, without overinvolvement. Adopting this position should reduce borderline symptoms as the patient's reactive role positions become less extreme.

The opposite process would be one in which the significant other dealing with the borderline patient has an unstable, unpredictable tendency toward extreme role positions, such as good-bad and loved-hated. This would be mirrored in increased instability between polarities in the patient, with increased tendency to extreme role positions. This may be the etiological process if it occurs in the relationship between mother and child. The mother, for example, may alternate between devaluing and idealizing behavior. Thus, the mother's emotional state is determined by her psychopathology with its conflicting extremes, making her unable to be responsive to the infant. The implication is that the psychopathology in the mother is along the borderline spectrum. The nature of the pathogenic role of the borderline mother would influence all stages of development, and would have an impact on various levels of the mother-child relationship. The mother's alternation between idealization and devaluation would be one of many levels but would be an important component through its contribution to the essential feature of the borderline disorder: "a pattern of unstable and intense interpersonal relationships characterized by alternating between the extremes of over-idealization and devaluation" (American Psychiatric Association 1987, p. 347).

The differences and similarities among the theorists are summarized in Table 2-1. Table 2-1 shows that conflict is important in the first three theorists but not in the last two. Deficit in the self is important in the last three and not the first two theorists. The external object is more important to the theorists on the left of the spectrum; on the right, the emphasis is on the object only in relation to the self.

In psychotherapy, interpretations are emphasized by the first four theorists but not by the fifth. The process experience independent of understanding is more important on the right, especially for the last two theorists.

With respect to etiology, constitutional factors are emphasized mainly by the first theorist. Physical failure of the environment is emphasized by the first theorist but is recognized by the others as being important. Empathic failure is most emphasized by the theories to the right of the spectrum.

DISCUSSION

The etiological theories deal mainly with environmental failure in the form of deficient parental care. Generally, little attention is given to constitutional factors in etiology. Various forms of deficient parental care are described as impairments in meeting physiological and/or psychological needs. Empathic failures relate to factors like the parents' poor response to cues from the infant, their lack of support for separation-individuation, and their unrealistic images of their children.

There is a clear position that severe psychopathology is common among the family members. Maternal disturbance is addressed most, but forms of paternal disturbance are also described. Parental

Table 2-1. Summary of emphasis of theorists

Dimensions	Kernberg	Masterson	Gunderson	Adler/Buie	Dawson
Psychopathology					
Conflict	++	+	+	−	−
Deficit in self	−	−	++	++	++
External object	++	+	+	−	−
Object in relation to self	−	−	+	++	++
Psychotherapy					
Interpretations	++	++	++	++	−
Process	+	+	++	++	++
Etiology					
Genetic factors	++	−	+	++	−
Physical failure of environment	++	+	++	++	++
Empathic failure of environment	+	++	++	++	++

Note. The table summarizes the emphasis placed by each theorist on a number of dimensions. − = little emphasis;
+ = some emphasis; ++ = marked emphasis.

psychopathology results in overinvolved or neglectful patterns of care, but the nature of the disorder in the parents is nonspecific. Several constructs converge on the idea that the parental pathology is borderline in nature. This may not necessarily mean that the parents have a diagnosable borderline personality disorder but rather that they have some borderline traits, especially in their family relationships. The implications of the mothers having a borderline disorder must extend beyond Masterson's phase-specific failure. The borderline pathology in the parent manifests in a number of ways and has impact at all phases of development, including adolescence. Failure of support for separation-individuation is one manifestation, but there are others.

Splits of devaluations and idealizations will have impact from earliest infancy, and oscillations between them may be particularly pathogenic. This specifically leads to the interpersonal instability of these patients. Other borderline traits have impact on development and need to be explored, for example, the etiological significance of parental impulsiveness, lack of control of anger, and ambivalence about the parental role. The evidence for such specific psychopathology in the parent is not good, and it seems that a number of pathological states in the parents may give rise to this disorder because the parents fail to meet the infant's needs for nurturance and empathy (Links et al. 1988).

In conclusion, some theories of borderline disorder have been considered in terms of their models of etiology, psychopathology, and treatment. The models of psychopathology are not testable because of their high level of abstraction. They aid clinical work by providing frameworks of thought, but we cannot be certain of their validity. The models of etiology are partially testable because of their emphasis on environmental failure of adequate child care. Families can be assessed in studies that provide empirical evidence of their present characteristics, but we cannot be sure how well this reflects the early environment. Also, we cannot be sure that observed family pathology is not a reaction to a primary process in the patient. Prospective studies of at-risk families may be helpful. The models of treatment are testable, as they provide specific strategies that can be compared in controlled trials. They have real clinical value in providing options that can be used differentially.

REFERENCES

Adler G: The myth of the alliance with borderline patients. Am J Psychiatry 136:642–645, 1979

Adler G, Buie D: Aloneness and borderline psychopathology: the possible relevance of child development issues. Int J Psychoanal 60:83–96, 1979

American Psychiatric Association: Diagnostic and Statistical Manual for Mental Disorders, 3rd Edition, Revised. Washington, DC, American Psychiatric Association, 1987

Buie D, Adler G: The definitive treatment of the borderline personality. Int J Psychoanal Psychother 9:51–87, 1982

Dawson D: Treatment of the borderline patient: relationship management. Can J Psychiatry 33:370–374, 1988

Gunderson J: BPD. Washington, DC, American Psychiatric Press, 1984

Gunderson J, Englund D: Characterizing the families of borderlines. Psychiatr Clin North Am 4:159–168, 1981

Gunderson J, Kerr J, Englund D: The families of borderlines: a comparative study. Arch Gen Psychiatry 37:27–33, 1980

Kernberg O: Borderline personality organization. J Am Psychoanal Assoc 15:641–685, 1967

Kernberg O: The treatment of patients with borderline personality organization. Int J Psychoanal 49:600–619, 1968

Links PS, Steiner M, Huxley G: The occurrence of borderline personality disorder in the families of borderline patients. Journal of Personality Disorders 2:14–20, 1988

Mahler M, LaPerriere K: Mother-child interaction during separation-individuation. Psychoanal Q 34:483–489, 1965

Masterson J: Treatment of the Borderline Adolescent: A Developmental Approach. New York, John Wiley, 1972

Masterson J: The borderline adolescent, in Adolescent Psychiatry: Developmental and Clinical Studies, Vol II. Edited by Feinstein SC, Giovacchini P. New York, Basic Books, 1973, pp 240–268

Masterson J, Rinsley D: The borderline syndrome: the role of the mother in the genesis and psychic structure of the borderline personality. Int J Psychoanal 56:163–177, 1975

Munroe Blum H, Marziali E, Links PS: A randomized clinical trial of specific time-limited group treatment of borderline patients. Grant from Ontario Mental Health Foundation, 1987–1989

Munroe Blum H, Marziali E, Links PS, et al: Continuation of a randomized controlled trial of relationship management group treatment for borderline patients. Grant from Health and Welfare Canada, 1990–1992

Waldinger RJ: Intensive psychodynamic therapy with borderline patients: an overview. Am J Psychiatry 144:267–274, 1987

Winnicott D: The theory of the parent-infant relationship. Int J Psychoanal 41:585–595, 1960

Chapter 3

Assessment of Interpersonal Factors in Borderline Pathology

Elsa Marziali, Ph.D.
Heather Munroe Blum, Ph.D.

Chapter 3

Assessment of Interpersonal Factors in Borderline Pathology

B orderline character disorders rank among the most difficult patient groups to diagnose and treat. There is no uniform criteria method for determining the diagnosis and no agreement as to the most effective treatment approaches. In fact, the treatment most frequently recommended (long-term dynamic psychotherapy) has produced limited results (McGlashan 1984). It is postulated that a focus on defining interpersonal factors unique to borderline functioning might bridge the knowledge-practice gaps that occur between diagnostic formulations, recommended treatments, and expectable outcomes.

The classification or diagnosis of any psychological disorder should serve two functions: communication and prognosis (Goodwin and Guze 1984). Diagnosis should distinguish features unique to the disorder, and it should predict the course of illness, treatment specificity, and expected outcomes. Few psychiatric diagnoses are based on explicit criteria supported by empirical data from follow-up studies. The DSM-III-R (American Psychiatric Association 1987) Axis II criteria for diagnosing borderline character disorder are no exception insofar as these criteria are not specific to the disorder, nor can they be used to infer etiology, course of illness, or treatment type and affects. Rather, the DSM-III-R Axis II borderline criteria are descriptors of symptomatic and behavioral phenomena that apply to a heterogeneous group of psychiatric disorders. Even when standardized methods such as structured interview schedules (Personality Disorder Examination [Loranger et al. 1987], Personality Disorders Questionnaire [Hyler et al. 1978], Structured Interview for DSM-III Personality Disorders [Stangl et al. 1985]) are used to apply borderline criteria, the problem of overlap with other disorders remains. Community and clinic surveys have demonstrated that, in general, there is a high rate of multiple psychiatric diagnoses among psychiatric cases (Weissman et al. 1986; Wing et al. 1981), and multiple diagnoses may be the norm for patients with borderline character disorders (Akiskal 1981; Gunderson and Kolb 1978; Links 1982; Perry 1985). What features of borderline personality disorder (BPD), if any, might be useful in predicting the clinical course of the disorder and response to treatment?

There are eight DSM-III-R criteria (p. 347) for BPD:

1. A pattern of unstable and intense interpersonal relationships characterized by alternating between extremes of overidealization and devaluation
2. Impulsiveness in at least two areas that are potentially self-damaging
3. Affective instability
4. Inappropriate, intense anger or lack of control of anger
5. Recurrent suicidal threats, gestures, or behavior, or self-mutilating behavior
6. Marked and persistent identity disturbance manifested by uncertainty about at least two of the following: self-image, sexual orientation, long-term goals or career choice, type of friends desired, preferred values
7. Chronic feelings of emptiness or boredom
8. Frantic efforts to avoid real or imagined abandonment

Of these, unstable and intense interpersonal relationships and persistent identity diffusion can be classified as containing interpersonal dimensions. However, because a patient can qualify for the diagnosis on the basis of any subset of five criteria, the interpersonal dimensions may or may not play a role in assigning the diagnosis. Only recently have there been attempts to examine whether or not the eight criteria are applied in uniform subsets for determining presence or absence of the disorder. Clarkin and Hurt (1988) used an agglomerative cluster analysis to generate subsets of criteria used in the clinical diagnosis of 451 borderline patients. Three clusters were identified: 1) an Identity Cluster, which included identity disturbance and chronic feelings of emptiness; 2) an Affective Cluster, which included labile affect, unstable interpersonal relations, and inappropriate anger; and 3) an Impulsive Cluster, which included self-damaging acts and impulsivity. When the observed prevalence of cluster pairs was assessed for each patient, the Affective-Impulsive cluster pairing occurred much more frequently than could be expected by chance. Thus, the borderline disorder is best defined by three criteria: 1) unstable relationships, 2) affect instability, and 3) impulsive behavior. These analyses show that the interpersonal factor is an especially important contributor to the diagnosis of BPD. In addition, problems with processing emotions (affect instability) and maladaptive defensive operations (impulsive behavior) are important dimensions for an understanding of the nature of the pathological behaviors.

An alternate diagnostic perspective from the DSM-III-R criteria method emphasizes the dynamic/structural features of personality organization. Kernberg (1975) specifies three intrapsychic organizing principles common to severe personality disorders: 1) identity diffusion, 2) primitive defensive operations, and 3) intact capacity for reality testing. According to Kernberg, these criteria are associated with etiological and early child developmental phenomena, and they predict course and expected outcome of treatment. Of the three criteria, Kernberg believes that identity diffusion most clearly differentiates borderline from nonborderline conditions (Kernberg 1980). Other clinicians use similar dynamic, diagnostic criteria to predict treatment type and duration (Buie and Adler 1982; Giovacchini 1979; Waldinger and Gunderson 1987), course of illness (Gunderson 1984; McGlashan 1985), and treatment response (Adler 1979; Gunderson 1984), but these have been subjected to only minimal testing.

Despite agreement among clinicians on the dynamic formulation of borderline personality organization, perspectives of etiologic and developmental precursors vary. Most clinicians acknowledge the possible influence of genetic/constitutional factors but differ as to the primacy of certain developmental features in determining the presence of borderline pathology in adults. In addition, it is likely that there exist multiple causal pathways to the condition of BPD. Kernberg (1975) believes that the lack of resolution of a core conflict in early development is a contributor to borderline disorder. An excessive aggressive drive (inborn or reactive to the environment) fails to be integrated with libidinal strivings. Primitive defenses are mobilized to keep separate conflicted perceptions of self and others. Kernberg's model presumes that a beginning capacity for object constancy and self-other differentiation has been acquired. Kernberg associates the occurrence of borderline pathology with unresolved problems of the separation-individuation subphase of Mahler's (1971a) rapprochement stage of early development. In contrast, the "deficit theorists" (Buie and Adler 1982; Gunderson 1984) believe that the borderline patient has not experienced an environment that could support the development of a stable self-identity in relation to a perception of an independent other. From this perspective, the borderline patient is perceived as playing out in interpersonal relationships a persistent struggle to attain object constancy.

From this brief sketch of different approaches for diagnosing borderline patients it is clear that, in their current form, no criteria system is adequate for inferring etiology or predicting course of illness and types and effects of treatments. On the other hand, the various approaches share an acknowledgment of the importance of interpersonal deviance as a key element of borderline disorder. If a deviant interpersonal schema is a core feature of what is known as borderline disorder, this feature may be dominant or subordinate depending on the nature of any comorbidity. It is proposed that more emphasis be placed on exploring the interpersonal dimensions that are pertinent to understanding and treating these difficult to engage and manage patients. An interpersonal focus would emphasize relationship issues that have immediate value for engaging the borderline patient in a treatment contract and that could serve as markers of treatment outcome. Regardless of the forms of treatment currently prescribed for borderline patients (psychiatric emergency services, hospitalization, pharmacotherapy, or psychotherapy), all depend on the formation of a therapeutic relationship that will sustain the patient throughout the treatment process, whatever its duration and aims. Thus, the assessment and classification of interpersonal issues hold promise for predicting the process and outcomes of all treatments currently recommended for borderline patients.

To address this task, several pathways need to be explored. If, for example, etiological factors are related to the borderline patient's problems in initiating and sustaining stable interpersonal relationships, how can this be demonstrated? Similarly, if a history of problems with identity diffusion and unstable interpersonal relationships has relevance for understanding course of illness and response to treatments, how are these variables best measured? Discussed below are strategies for isolating certain diagnostic factors that could be used to test hypothesized associations among etiological, behavioral, and dynamic factors from an interpersonal perspective.

RELEVANCE OF CONSTITUTIONAL / DEVELOPMENTAL FACTORS

In describing borderline pathology, several researchers draw inferences about the possible relevance of constitutional predisposing phenomena, including excessive aggressive drive (Kernberg 1975), basic defect in affect regulation (Klein 1977), and constitutional differences in attachment behaviors (Ainsworth et al. 1978). Yet there is no verifiable association between constitutional predisposition and the development of BPD in adults. Infant observational studies and longitudinal studies of early development hold promise for testing some aspects of the diathesis-pathology hypothesis. Current studies show that the neonate plays a significant role in determining the quality and quantity of interactions with caregivers. Studies show that these early patterns of interpersonal contact appear to provide experiential templates on which subsequent models of self-other relatedness are based (Waters et al. 1979).

Theories that link phase-specific developmental factors with the development of borderline pathology are, like the constitutional hypotheses, unverifiable in the absence of longitudinal studies of child-caregiver interactions in families identified as being at high risk for the development of psychological disorders. Despite the clinical formulation that associates the borderline syndrome with a developmental failure in Mahler's (1971a) rapprochement/separation-individuation subphase, Mahler (1971b) believed that problems identified during this stage of development were not specific to the occurrence of borderline pathology in adults. It may be less important to perpetuate speculation about the association between developmental conflicts/failures and more important to test in the adult whether or not the hypothesized pathological outcomes exist. For example, if identity diffusion is a major distinguishing feature of the borderline patient according to DSM-III-R and Kernberg (1975), which dimensions validate the construct and can they be demonstrated empirically? Is one aspect of identity diffusion concerned with an impaired ability to perceive self as separate from other? Are perceptual distortions about interpersonal boundaries associated with problems in identifying and processing emotions? Do defense mechanisms play a role in maintaining confused and emotionally charged mental representations of interpersonal relationships? Three categories of measurement strategies show promise for isolating interpersonal factors relevant to the diagnosis and treatment of BPD: 1) broad spectrum measures of interpersonal phenomena, 2) measures of emotion recognition and emotion processing, and 3) measures of mental representations of self in relation to others.

BROAD SPECTRUM MEASURES OF INTERPERSONAL PHENOMENA

An interpersonal behavior classification system of psychological disorders has been proposed by Benjamin (1981, 1987) and McLemore and Benjamin (1979): the Structured Analysis of Social Behaviour (SASB). Benjamin has developed a circumplex model of social behavior variables, which are depicted on two orthogonal axes that represent clusters of opposing behaviors. Each of three surfaces (circles) displays the circumplex ordering of 36 behaviors. One surface depicts interpersonal behaviors that focus on the other person in the interaction. A second surface focuses on the self, and the third surface portrays an inward reflection of the self-other paradigms represented in the first two surfaces. On each surface, the horizontal axis contains a spectrum of affiliative-disaffiliative behaviors, and the vertical axis reflects independence versus control. The full model presumes interpersonal complementary; that is, a given interpersonal action tends to pull for a similar reaction (corresponding) on the affiliative dimension, and an opposite reaction (reciprocal) on the control dimension. For example, "affirming and understanding" evokes "disclosing and expressing," and "ignoring and neglecting" evokes "walling off and distancing."

The measure can be used by trained judges to code an observed interaction on the other and the self surfaces. A questionnaire version can be completed by a patient, the patient's family members, or a therapist. The responses are keyed to behaviors on each circumplex surface. Test-retest reliabilities for the questionnaire version and interrater reliabilities for judgments of observed interactions are high (range .85 to .93).

The SASB system provides information about a patient's reactive responses in interpersonal interactions and more enduring portrayals of the meanings of interpersonal interactions when they are reflected inwardly. The model translates psychoanalytic ideas about introjected self-object relations into geometric terms that show specifically how interpersonal experiences affect perceptions of oneself. The breadth and depth of analysis of interpersonal phenomena provided by the SASB addresses several of the shortcomings of the DSM-III-R Axis II diagnostic method. The SASB system does not require adherence to any etiological position; rather, it suggests continuity between normal and pathological behavior. Consequently, it has considerable value for prognosis, specification of treatment, and the prediction of change.

Benjamin (in press) has used the SASB system to provide dimensional analyses of Axis II diagnostic types. Representative items from the questionnaire SASB method have been matched with Axis II descriptors for BPD. For each of the eight criteria, Benjamin provides interpersonal descriptors. She demonstrates how these are especially useful to a therapist for understanding and anticipating the patient's psychological demands on the treatment relationship. In another study, Benjamin (1989) used the questionnaire method to assess differences in interpersonal patterns between patient groups. Borderline, bipolar depressed, and unipolar depressed patients rated themselves, their parents, and a significant other at their "best" and at their "worst." Significant between-group differences in pattern coefficients showed that the interpersonal experiences of each group were different. For example, the borderline patients saw their mothers as being overly attacking. This contrasted with the other two groups, who saw their mothers as being more friendly. Also, the borderline patients believed that they received far more conflicting messages from their mothers. This work is in progress; thus, the contribution of the SASB model for understanding interpersonal dimensions as they apply to diagnostic and treatment issues will need to be supported in future treatment trials of borderline patients that test different models of treatment.

Research on the SASB system could test the types of complementary and reciprocal behaviors engaged in during phases of treatment with borderline patients. Furthermore, shifts in these interactions following a course of treatment would show changes, if any, from disaffiliative/control interpersonal interactions to more affiliative/independent self-other transactions. The direction of these shifts could be predicted *a priori*. Also, therapist behaviors that evoke hostile, controlling behaviors from the patient could be distinguished from therapist actions that encourage friendly, independent patient responses. The tracking of these factors as they evolve in treatment would expand considerably our understanding of the treatment encounter and would explore why therapy with borderline patients is so frequently doomed to failure.

The "core conflictual relationship theme" (CCRT) method developed by Luborsky et al. (1985) provides a systematic procedure for evaluating relationship patterns. The method is especially relevant for clinicians because the data necessary for assessing the CCRT dimensions are contained in discussions about the patient's significant relationships as they evolve in the natural course of an assessment or treatment interview. Narratives about relationships provide the unit of analysis. Each narrative makes reference to an important person with whom the patient interacts. The important person is usually any one of the following: parent, sibling, friend, boss, or the therapist. Within each object narrative, the patient's wishes, needs, and intentions toward the other person can be inferred and rated. In addition, the responses from the other person and the self reactions/responses can be isolated. The same method for generating the person, the wish, the response from other, and the response from self is applied across relationship episodes to yield a summary of frequencies for each component. From the highest frequencies, a core relationship theme is constructed.

Luborsky developed and tested the method on transcribed treatment sessions of patients in psychoanalytically oriented psychotherapy. The CCRT method was applied to relationship episodes from two early and two late sessions. The results showed that there is usually one main CCRT that is based on the higher frequency of occurrence of one theme over all others. Each patient has a unique CCRT that is reflected across key interpersonal relationships. The CCRT is repeated in the relationship with the therapist. The CCRT changes during the course of psychotherapy; the wishes change less than the responses from other, and less than the responses from self. For improved patients, the expected responses from self and from other were more negative early in the therapy and more positive later in the therapy. Themes that were generated from relationship episodes in which a parent was the object and that were repeated in relationship episodes with a current important person supported the historical nature of deviant as well as normal patterns of interpersonal phenomena.

The CCRT method can be applied reliably by trained judges. It has appeal as a method that can be used readily by clinicians in diagnostic and early treatment sessions to infer the main relationship theme(s) that is of central concern to the patient and that is reflected in the treatment relationship. This provides a focus for the exploratory/interpretive work of the therapy. Also, the therapist can anticipate the relationship themes that are likely to be repeated in the treatment encounter.

Until recently, the CCRT method had not been used to differentiate diagnostic groups, but Luborsky et al. (1985) attempted to estimate the differences between the CCRTs of patients who differed in levels of severity of psychiatric symptoms. He calculated the ratio of the frequency of appearance of a theme in an episode to all episodes as a way of designating the degree of stereotypy of relationship themes. His impression is that "the greater the stereotypy, the greater the psychiatric severity of the diagnosis and the more difficult to modify the pattern" (p. 245).

Preliminary results of a study in which the CCRT method was used with borderline and neurotic patients were recently reported by a group of investigators at Cornell (Schlefer et al. 1989). CCRTs were generated for a group of borderline patients diagnosed according to DSM-III-R criteria and for a comparison group of neurotic patients. As expected, the borderline patients' themes differed from the neurotic patients' themes. Of importance was the finding that the borderline CCRT themes generated by independent judges were similar to dynamic themes alleged clinically to be present in this patient group. This work is in progress. Future studies need to explore whether Luborsky's speculations about stereotyped CCRTs apply to all severe character disorders or if they are particularly evident in borderline patients. Also, whether stereotyped themes remain intractable, as Luborsky suggests, could be tested in a treatment trial with borderline patients. Are some forms of treatment more successful than others in altering borderline patients' negative object themes or deviant interpersonal transactions? It is likely that different treatments will be required to obtain change on different dimensions of the interpersonal paradigm. Recognition of the discrete factors that define interpersonal dysfunction (such as the CCRT dimensions) underscores the need to measure these phenomena as well as symptom outcomes in treatment effectiveness studies of borderline disorder.

MEASURES OF EMOTIONAL RECOGNITION AND EMOTION PROCESSING

Clinically borderline patients demonstrate that they have great difficulty in recognizing accurately their own and others' emotions. They have little tolerance for intense emotions, and are unable to communicate clearly what it is that they feel at any point in time. Of the eight DSM-III-R diagnostic criteria for BPD, three refer directly to problems with emotion processing (anger, emptiness, affective instability), and three other criteria are reactions to emotions (impulsivity, self-harming behaviors, and avoidance of being alone). There has been little effort focused on the empirical validation of the emotion-processing component of borderline pathology.

In the past decade, child development research has explored the parallels between developmental pathways through which emotions are processed and Piaget's (1962) stages of cognitive operations. In these studies, emotions are defined as the primary motivational forces in all human interaction. Emotions provide the organizing principles for interpersonal relating (Emde and Sorce 1983); in particular, they are the cognitive affective structures that determine the quality of attachments and the conditions of separations (Lewis 1988). Emde and Sorce (1983) and Demos (1988) have explored emotional expression in young children (neonate to 2 years) and found that infants' facial movements correspond to expected patterns of expression of basic emotions. Fitzpatrick (1985) and Harris (1985) have shown that children develop a logical system of emotional constructs during the operational and preoperational stages of development (ages 2 to

7 years). Feelings are external to the self and are bound to events. For example, happiness "arrives" with a gift and "leaves" when the gift is taken away. Children in this age group do not understand emotions as internal experiences, nor are they able to process simultaneously positive and negative feelings (Gnepp et al. 1987; Harter and Buddin 1987). Between the ages of 7 and 12 years (concrete operational stage), children provide more refined definitions of feelings. They are able to separate feelings arising from internal states from feelings associated with external events. Also, feelings within the self are differentiated from feelings in others, even when they are discrepant (Selman 1980). By age 10, children are able to recognize the experience of oppositely valenced emotions toward the same event, but a true capacity for ambivalence is not integrated until early adolescence (Harter and Buddin 1987).

Studies of emotion processing in children from disturbed families show that these children are less accurate in determining the feelings of peers, and they recognize anger more frequently than happiness (Camras et al. 1983; Richenbach and Masters 1983). Camras et al. speculate that the study children were impaired in their capacity to decode feelings expressed by peers because of the inconsistent manner in which feelings were expressed by their parents.

Less research effort has been devoted to examining how adults understand and process emotions. There have been no attempts to replicate in adult studies models for processing emotions that would parallel the child development phases of emotion recognition and integration. Yet studies of emotions in adults could be useful for testing clinical hypotheses about how borderline patients experience and manage feelings, and for guiding treatment. For example, are there parallels between the borderline patient's capacity for processing emotions and the capacity demonstrated by children in the preoperational and operational stages of development? That is, are feelings "event bound" and externally determined? Have borderline patients failed to achieve the capacity for recognizing feelings in the self as separate from others (concrete operational stage)? Could it be demonstrated empirically that borderline patients have difficulty processing ambivalent feelings? Currently, answers to these questions are inferred from clinical observations. Empirical validation of these hypotheses would provide tools for refining criteria used to diagnose borderline patients. New measures of emotion processing could be used in longitudinal studies of the course of illness. Finally, the study of emotion responses in borderline patients would contribute to the development of more effective treatment models. For example, the study of "expressed emotions," which has been applied to families of schizophrenic patients (Leff and Vaughn 1985), may provide a model for studying the responses of borderline patients to intense emotions in interpersonal contacts.

Studies of emotion processing would need to include explorations of mechanisms of defense. The question to be addressed is the following: Do certain defense operations come into play when certain emotions are experienced? Psychodynamic formulations of borderline pathology emphasize the role played by "primitive defenses" in explaining the etiology and psychological structure of severe character disorders. Primitive denial, idealization, projective identification, and devaluation are the defenses typically ascribed to borderline functioning (Giovacchini 1979; Kernberg 1975; Meissner 1984). Empirical tests of the defense-pathology hypothesis are especially important because the therapies currently recommended for borderline patients (long-term, dynamic psychotherapy) are determined on the basis of the merits of interpreting defensive operations (Kernberg 1975) versus tolerating and empathetically resonating defense behaviors (Buie and Adler 1982).

Although several methods have been developed for empirically assessing defense mechanisms (Bond et al. 1983; Bond and Vaillant 1986; Vaillant and Vaillant 1986), only one study has examined defenses specific to borderline disorders. Perry and Cooper (1985, 1986) developed the Clinical Defense Mechanism Rating Scales to rate 22 defense mechanisms that capture immature, borderline, and neurotic levels of defensive functioning. The scales were tested on borderline and two near-neighbor disorders: antisocial and bipolar type II affective disorders. Psychodynamic interviews conducted with 72 subjects were videotaped and rated on the defense scales by trained judges. Defense mechanisms that were empirically correlated were combined into five summary defense scales: 1) disavowal, 2) action, 3) borderline, 4) narcissistic, and 5) obsessional. Each summary defense scale was correlated with diagnostic variables for the borderline and affective disorder groups. The borderline and action defenses correlated significantly with the borderline diagnostic group. In contrast, the narcissistic defenses correlated significantly with the affective disorder group but not with the borderline group. However, none of the five summary defense scales discriminated the three diagnostic groups.

In a related study, Perry and Cooper (1986) examined the associations between defense mechanisms and future psychosocial functioning in 55 subjects who were part of the original cohort mentioned above. They found that eight borderline level defenses tended to predict negative outcomes in terms of work, interpersonal relating, and personal satisfaction. The action defenses were the most powerful predictors of poorer outcome and the increased likelihood of psychosocial impairment.

Studies are needed to examine the linkages between defensive operations used by borderline patients and problems with emotion recognition and integration. Which defenses are associated with processing which emotions? Are defensive patterns consistent across interpersonal relationships? Do they persist over time? Do particular models of psychotherapy alter the processing of emotions and/or the associated patterns of defensive operations?

MEASURES OF MENTAL REPRESENTATIONS OF SELF IN RELATION TO OTHERS

Both the DSM-III-R and psychodynamic criteria methods for diagnosing borderline character disorders include identity disturbance as one feature for distinguishing the disorder. The DSM-III-R operational definition of this criterion includes uncertainty about self identity, self image, sexual orientation, career goals, preferred friendships, values, and loyalties. Kernberg (1975) describes similar diagnostic criteria as "identity diffusion," which includes lack of integration of the concept of the self and of significant others, chronic feelings of emptiness, contradictory perceptions of self in relation to others, and difficulties in describing features in the self that are different from features observed in others. The inference to be drawn from both criteria systems is that mental health assumes a capacity for developing and maintaining accurate and stable mental images of the self as separate from others. Measures that isolate levels in this capacity would be useful for studying diagnostic factors relevant to the borderline disorder. In addition, such measures would have predictive functions for locating change in this dimension following a course of treatment.

The concept of the object in relation to the self has been studied from a variety of perspectives. Blatt and Lerner (1983) have coded human responses on the Rorschach on a scale developed by Blatt to provide a developmental analysis of the concept of the object. The scale dimensions include differentiation, articulation, and integration. The responses of groups of neurotic, borderline, and schizophrenic patients showed distinct between-group differences. The Rorschach responses of the borderline patients showed unremitting hypervigilance, heightened sensitivity, and excessive vulnerability. Mayman (1968) has attempted in a similar fashion to capture interpersonal dimensions through the analysis of early memories. The problem with these methods is the lack of interpersonal stimuli in the content of the analysis; that is, the material produced by the subject (Rorschach responses, reports of early memories) do not necessarily depict interpersonal interactions. Even when descriptions contain human representations, the nature of the object relations can only be inferred indirectly. These systems tend to yield global assessments of object relatedness, and scale subdimensions, if any, are not well defined.

In an effort to address the shortcomings of several projective techniques, Burke et al. (1986) devised the Comprehensive Object Relations Profile (CORP). It is a semistructured projective test that was designed to measure three separate dimensions of a subject's capacity to relate to others: 1) object constancy, 2) object integration, and 3) emphathic capacity. The operational definitions of each dimension are particularly relevant for assessing relational deficits in borderline patients. For example, object integration refers to the degree to which both positively and negatively valenced affects can be perceived in relationships with others. Also, the definition of empathy contains two dimensions: 1) subjectivity, which refers to the degree to which the respondent can perceive thoughts and feelings of another person; and 2) appreciation, which refers to the degree to which the respondent can understand reasons for the perceived subjective state.

The CORP stimuli consist of six interpersonal vignettes. The respondent is asked to assume that he or she is a particular character in the vignette and then is asked to respond to a number of questions designed to measure one or more of the four object-relation dimensions. Each vignette portrays a particular interpersonal setting and a particular conflict within that setting. A score is given for each of the four dimensions (object constancy, integration, empathic subjectivity, and appreciation). Burke et al. compared CORP responses of groups of schizophrenic, borderline, and neurotic patients clinically diagnosed based on DSM-III criteria. The scale scores for the four dimensions and the composite scores differentiated the three diagnostic groups. The empathy subscale dimension, which included the ability to perceive and appreciate another's point of view, was the dimension that most powerfully distinguished mild from severe psychopathology. The neurotic group showed, more clearly than the severely pathological groups, a capacity to form a distinct and integrated image of the other.

Another projective technique developed by Hansburg and Henry (1980) was designed as a diagnostic tool to capture adolescents' responses to separation and loss. Hansburg and Henry based their work on the assumption that an individual's projected reactions to separations and losses would be indicative of both the quality of object-relation functioning and the capacity for differentiating a self identity separate from others. Thus, the central developmental dimension measured by Hansburg and Henry's Separation Anxiety Test (SAT) is separation-individuation. The SAT consists of 12 black and white ink drawings, each depicting a child undergoing a different separation experience. Six of the separation portrayals are designated as mild because they represent typical separations that any child under 6 years would be expected to manage with minimal distress. The other six pictures are designated as strong because they represent traumatic events such as permanent losses. Each picture has a list of 17 statements that describe how the child might be feeling or reacting. Each statement is an operational equivalent of 1 of 17 psychic mechanisms rooted in Bowlby's theory of attachment and loss (1973).

In a series of studies, Hansburg established both the reliability and validity of the measure for classifying respondents according to six systems of response: 1) attachment, 2) individuation, 3) painful tension, 4) hostility, 5) defensive operations, and 6) self evaluation. The test has shown significant differences in the expected direction for the six dimensions, among the following:

- Adolescents from intact families, and institutionalized, self-destructive, and acting out adolescents (Hansburg 1976)
- Elderly persons actively involved in work and social situations, and elderly living in nursing homes (Hansburg 1978)
- Child-abusing mothers and typical mothers (DeLozier 1979)
- Groups of individuals with pathology suggestive of problems with separation-individuation, and normal controls (Braver 1983; Schwartz 1980)

The measure has also been used to test the association between intimacy capacity and separation-individuation (Levitz-Jones and Orlotsky 1985). Although the SAT has not been tested with borderline character disorders, it appears to be a useful instrument for locating psychological dimensions associated with the intense conflicts experienced by borderline patients in interpersonal relationships. The predictive validity of the measure, especially following an intervention, has yet to be established. It would be important to show change, if any, in the six scale dimensions following treatment of borderline patients with those treatments that purport to effect change on interpersonal dimensions (Giovacchini 1979; Kernberg 1975).

The above reviewed measures of interpersonal conflict dimensions all rely on projective or semiprojective techniques for generating the subjects' responses. Blatt devised an alternate method for measuring the capacity for object relating based on estimates of a subject's level of achievement of psychological separation-individuation (Blatt 1974; Blatt et al. 1979, 1981). The method has clinical appeal because the data used to generate level scores are based on a subject's description of a significant other—a parent. Thus, rather than inferring levels of interpersonal dimensions from responses to projective stimuli, Blatt expects the subject to produce the same material that a clinician would elicit to determine the subject's capacity for interpersonal relating. Blatt and his colleagues developed a scoring method that locates five levels of differentiation of self from other. In ascending order, the scale depicts degrees of psychological independence between self and other, ranging from undifferentiated (Level I) to stable differentiated (Level V). The scale is based on an integration of psychoanalytic theory (Jacobson 1964; Mahler 1971a) and cognitive developmental psychology (Piaget 1955; Werner and Kaplan 1963). From this combined perspective, it is postulated that in the course of development, cognitive-affective representations of self and other provide the nuclei around which character structure is built. Blatt's scale can be viewed as a developmental hierarchy in which higher levels indicate more complete self-other differentiation—the necessary condition for mature character formation. Conversely, at lower levels there is less differentiation accompanied by pathological character formation. Blatt et al. (1979) tested the object representational method on a group of 123 college students in order to assess associations between representations of parents and depression. Two judges assigned a level score to the parental descriptions. The interjudge reliabilities and the concurrent, construct, and predictive validity of the measure were found to be adequate. Depression was related to quality of parental descriptions as hypothesized.

Blatt's methodology for estimating levels of object representation was extended and tested on a cohort of borderline patients (Marziali and Oleniuk 1990). In Blatt's method, a single level score is given. Thus, the method assumes that a subject's level of object representation is unitary, that is, one score largely describes the overall level of achievement of self-other differentiation. In contrast, the new scoring method was based on the assumption that in each individual there are multiple levels of conceptual representations of significant others. The responses of five borderline patients who qualified for the diagnosis on the Diagnostic Interview for Borderline patients

(Gunderson et al. 1981), the Personality Disorder Examination (Loranger et al. 1987), and the Personality Disorders Questionnaire (Hyler et al. 1986) were compared with the responses of five non-psychiatric subjects. An interview guide was used to elicit from each subject descriptions of a parent and a current important other person. Whereas Blatt used the entire description of an object to provide one level score, in the new method each phrase of the transcribed descriptions was used as the coding unit. Each unit was assigned one of five level codes. A detailed coding manual was developed. The five levels of object representation are operationalized as follows. At Level I, the object is described mainly in subjective terms. The concern is whether the object gratifies or frustrates the subject's needs. At Level II, the description of the object is literal, concrete, and often of physical features. At Level III, the description shows that the respondent can use symbols and signs to represent the object. These symbol images are based on an appreciation of the object's functions, activities, or specific attributes. At Level IV, symbols are used to reflect an understanding of the object's internal thoughts, feelings, and attitudes. At Level V, a more complex conceptual representation of other is revealed. Contradictions within the object are noted, and the capacity for change over time is appreciated.

For each subject, a profile of five level scores for each of the two objects was generated. Level scores were generated by summing the number of phrases for each of the codes assigned and dividing by the total number of phrases in the transcript. In this manner, a proportion of response for each level was obtained. Following 20 hours of training, adequate between-judge agreement was achieved (average kappa coefficient .65). The results showed that all five level scores were assigned to the descriptions of both groups, borderline and nonpsychiatric. The profiles of the descriptions of parents and important current other were analyzed separately and in combination. The findings showed that, as predicted, the borderline group had higher frequencies of responses in the lower levels of object representation (Levels I and II) and the nonpsychiatric group had more responses at the higher levels (Levels III and IV). Although the borderline patients received more codes in the less differentiated range of images of self in relation to others, they also received codes at the more differentiated level of object representation (Levels III and IV). Given these findings, it is expected that the new coding method could be used to assess shifts in object representational profiles over time, especially following an intervention such as psychotherapy. Shifts might reasonably take place in the central range of the scale (Levels II and III). For a chart display of the all measures, see Table 3-1.

CONCLUSIONS

The study of interpersonal phenomena in borderline pathology requires a multidimensional approach. The dimensions include

- The quality of manifest interpersonal behaviors
- Patterns of core interpersonal conflicts
- Capacity for processing complex emotions
- Patterns of defensive operations
- The capacity for differentiating mental images of others from perceptions of the self

Measurement technology is sufficiently advanced to permit the examination of these dimensions under various study conditions: longitudinal studies of children in high-risk families, treatment con-

Table 3-1. Measures of interpersonal factors

Authors	Focus	Psychometric properties
Benjamin 1981, 1987; McLemore and Benjamin 1979	Multidimensional, circumplex model of interpersonal behaviors	Test-retest, interrater reliability, and validity studies
Luborsky et al. 1985	Analysis of interpersonal narratives	Interrater reliability; validity studies in progress
Gnepp et al. 1987; Harter and Buddin 1987	Measures of developmental levels of emotion processing (tested with children only)	Rater reliability, replication, and cross-validation
Perry and Cooper 1985; Bond et al. 1983; Vaillant and Vaillant 1986	Methods for identifying defense mechanisms	Some reliability and discriminant validity studies
Hansburg 1976; Blatt et al. 1979; Burke et al. 1986; Marziali and Oleniuk 1990	Measures of levels of mental representation of self in relation to other	Reliability studies; validity studies in progress

trol trials with borderline patients, and longitudinal studies of course of illness. The five dimensions are intrinsically linked and require simultaneous exploration.

No assessment or treatment of borderline patients can proceed without taking into account the effects of the interpersonal dimensions of borderline disorder. The presenting problems of the borderline patient consistently include difficulties in the interpersonal sphere. A deviant interpersonal schema may be a core feature of borderline disorder that may be dominant or subordinate to comorbidity. Regardless of the context of the treatment environment (hospital milieu, pharmacotherapy, psychotherapy, or environmental manipulation), the challenge to the therapist is the management of the treatment relationship with the borderline patient. Studies that validate the unique ways in which borderline patients process information in interpersonal transactions would advance the repertoire of intervention strategies needed to treat effectively these difficult-to-manage patients. Treatment studies of BPD should include social (interpersonal) as well as clinical outcomes.

REFERENCES

Adler G: The myth of the alliance with borderline patients. Am J Psychiatry 136:642–645, 1979

Ainsworth MD, Blehan MC, Waters E, et al: Patterns of Attachment. Hillsdale, NJ, Erlbaum, 1978

Akiskal HS: Subaffective disorders: dysthymic, cyclothymic and bipolar II disorders in the "borderline realm." Psychiatr Clin North Am 4:25–46, 1981

American Psychiatric Association: Diagnostic and Statistical Manual of Mental Disorders, 3rd Edition, Revised. Washington, DC, American Psychiatric Association, 1987

Benjamin LS: Structural analysis of social behaviour. Psychol Rev 81:392–425, 1981

Benjamin LS: Use of the SASB dimensional model to develop treatment plans for personality disorders. I: Narcissism. Journal of Personality Disorders 1:43–70, 1987

Benjamin LS: Usefulness of measures of social perception to distinguish among depressed persons with borderline personality, unipolar and bipolar mood disorders. Unpublished manuscript, 1989

Benjamin LS: Structural Analysis of Interactional Patterns in Personality Disorders. New York, Guilford (in press)

Blatt SJ: Levels of object representation and introjective depression. Psychoanal Study Child 29:107–157, 1974

Blatt SJ, Lerner H: The psychological assessment of object representation. J Pers Assess 47:7–28, 1983

Blatt SJ, Wein SJ, Chevron E, et al: Parental representations in depression in normal young adults. J Abnorm Psychol 88:388–397, 1979

Blatt SJ, Chevron ES, Quinlan DM, et al: The Assessment of Qualitative and Structural Dimensions of Object Representations. Unpublished manual, 1981

Bond MP, Vaillant SJ: An empirical study of the relationship between diagnosis and defense style. Arch Gen Psychiatry 43:285–288, 1986

Bond M, Gardner ST, Christian J, et al: Empirical study of self-rated defense styles. Arch Gen Psychiatry 40:333–338, 1983

Bowlby J: Attachment and Loss, Vol II: Separation Anxiety and Anger. New York, Basic Books, 1973

Braver MD: The attachment dimension in schizophrenia. Dissertation Abstracts International 44:1951B, 1983 (University Microfilms No 8323814)

Buie D, Adler G: The definitive treatment of the borderline personality. Int J Psychoanal Psychother 33:531–546, 1982

Burke WF, Summers F, Selinger D, et al: The comprehensive object relations profile: a preliminary report. Psychoanalytic Psychology 3:173–185, 1986

Camras L, Grow J, Rebordy S: Recognition of emotional expression by abused children. Journal of Clinical Child Psychology 12:325–328, 1983

Clarkin J, Hurt SW: Subclassification of borderline personality disorder: a cluster solution. Paper presented at the annual meeting of the Society of Psychotherapy Research, Santa Fe, NM, June 1988

DeLozier PP: An application of attachment theory to the study of child abuse. Doctoral dissertation, California School of Professional Psychology, Los Angeles, 1979

Demos V: Affect and the development of the self: a new frontier, in Progress in Self Psychology, Vol 3. Edited by Goldberg A. New York, Guilford, 1988, pp 27–33

Emde RN, Sorce JE: The rewards of infancy: emotional availability and maternal referencing, in Frontiers of Infant Psychiatry, Vol 2. Edited by Call JD, Galenson E, Tyson R. New York, Basic Books, 1983, pp 17–30

Fitzpatrick CJ: Children's development out of event-bound conceptions of their emotions, in Event Theory: A Piaget-Freud Integration. Edited by Fast I. Hillsdale, NJ, Erlbaum, 1985, pp 79–109

Giovacchini P: Treatment of Primitive Mental States. New York, Jason Aronson, 1979

Gnepp J, McKee E, Domanic J: Children's use of situational information to infer emotion: understanding emotionally equivocal situations. Developmental Psychology 23:114–123, 1987

Goodwin DW, Guze SB: Psychiatric Diagnosis. New York, Oxford University Press, 1984

Gunderson JG: Borderline Personality Disorder. Washington, DC, American Psychiatric Press, 1984

Gunderson JG, Kolb JE: Discriminating features of borderline patients. Am J Psychiatry 135:792–796, 1978

Gunderson JG, Kolb J, Austin V: The diagnostic interview for borderline patients. Am J Psychiatry 138:896–903, 1981

Hansburg HG: The use of the separation anxiety test in the detection of self-destructive tendencies in early adolescence, in Mental Health in Children, Vol II. Edited by Siva Sankar DV. Westbury, NY, PJD Publications, 1976, pp 161–199

Hansburg HG: Separation disorders of the elderly. Unpublished manuscript. New York, Jewish Child Care Association, 1978

Hansburg H, Henry G: Separation Disorders, I and II. New York, Robert E. Kreiger, 1980

Harris P: What children know about the situations that provoke emotion, in The Socialization of Emotions. Edited by Lewis M, Saarni C. New York, Plenum, 1985, pp 161–185

Harter S, Buddin B: Children's understanding of the simultaneity of two emotions: a five-stage developmental acquisition sequence. Developmental Psychology 23:390–399, 1987

Hyler SE, Rieder MD, Williams JB, et al: The Personality Diagnostic Questionnaire: A Comparison with Clinicians' DSM-III Diagnosis. New York, New York State Psychiatric Institute, 1986

Jacobson E; The Self and the Object World. New York, International Universities Press, 1964

Kernberg O: Borderline Conditions and Pathological Narcissism. New York, Jason Aronson, 1975

Kernberg O: Internal World and External Reality: Object Relations Theory Applied. New York, Jason Aronson, 1980

Klein DF: Psychopharmacological treatment and delineation of borderline disorders, in Borderline Personality Disorder: The Concept, the Syndrome, the Patient. Edited by Hartocollis P. New York, International Universities Press, 1977, pp 365–383

Leff J, Vaughn C: Expressed Emotion in Families. London, Guilford, 1985

Levitz-Jones EM, Orlotsky JL: Separation-individuation and intimacy capacity in college women. J Pers Soc Psychol 49:156–169, 1985

Lewis H: Freudian theory and new information in modern psychology. Psychoanalytic Psychology 5:7–22, 1988

Links P: The existence of the borderline diagnosis: studies on diagnostic validity. Can J Psychiatry 27:585–592, 1982

Loranger A, Susman V, Oldham J, et al: The Personality Disorder Examination: a preliminary report. Journal of Personality Disorders 1:1–13, 1987

Luborsky L, Melton J, Cohen K, et al: A verification of Freud's grandest clinical hypothesis: the transference. Clinical Psychology Review 5:231–246, 1985

Mahler MS: On Human Symbiosis and the Vicissitudes of Individuation. New York, International Universities Press, 1971a

Mahler MS: A study of the separation individuation process and its possible application to borderline phenomena in the psychoanalytic situation. Psychoanal Study Child 26:403–424, 1971b

Marziali E, Oleniuk J: Object representations in descriptions of significant others: a methodological study. J Pers Assess 54:105–115, 1990

Mayman M: Early memories and character structure. Journal of Projective Techniques and Personality Assessment 32:303–316, 1968

McGlashan T: The Chestnut Lodge follow-up study. II: Long term outcome of borderline personalities. Arch Gen Psychiatry 41:586–601, 1984

McGlashan T: The prediction of outcome in borderline personality disorder: part V of the Chestnut Lodge follow-up study, in The Borderline: Current Empirical Research. Edited by McGlashan T. Washington, DC, American Psychiatric Press, 1985, pp 63–98

McLemore CW, Benjamin LS: Whatever happened to interpersonal diagnosis? A psychosocial alternative to DSM-III. American Psychologist 34:17–34, 1979

Meissner WW: The Borderline Spectrum. New York, Jason Aronson, 1984

Perry JC: Depression in borderline personality disorder: lifetime prevalence at interview and longitudinal course of symptoms. Am J Psychiatry 142:15–21, 1985

Perry JC, Cooper SH: Psychodynamics, symptoms and outcome in borderline and antisocial personality disorders and bipolar type II affective disorder, in The Borderline: Current Empirical Research. Edited by McGlashan TH. Washington, DC, American Psychiatric Press, 1985, pp 19–42

Perry JC, Cooper SH: What do cross-sectional measures of defense mechanisms predict? in Empirical Studies of Ego Mechanisms of Defense. Edited by Vaillant GE. Washington, DC, American Psychiatric Press, 1986, pp 31–46

Piaget J: The Language and Thought of the Child. Translated by Gobain M. Cleveland OH, Meridian Books, 1955

Piaget J: Three lectures (The stages of intellectual development in the child; The relation of affectivity to intelligence in the mental development; Will and action). Bull Menninger Clin 26:120–145, 1962

Reichenbach L, Masters J: Children's use of expressive and contextual cues in judgements of emotion. Child Dev 54:993–1004, 1983

Schlefer EK, Selzer MA, Clarkin J, et al. CCRT: a method for comparing neurotics and borderlines. Paper presented at the annual meeting of the American Psychiatric Association, San Francisco, CA, May 1989

Schwartz P: A study of the relationship between attachment-separation and the fear of death. Dissertation Abstracts International, 41B:2302B, 1980 (University Microfilms No 8027391)

Selman RL: The growth of an interpersonal understanding of others. Developmental Psychology 22:649–654, 1980

Stangl D, Pfohl B, Zimmerman M, et al: A structured interview for the DSM-III personality disorders: a preliminary report. Arch Gen Psychiatry 42:591–596, 1985

Vaillant GE, Vaillant CD: A cross-validation of two empirical studies of defenses, in Empirical Studies of Ego Mechanisms of Defense. Edited by Vaillant GE. Washington, DC, American Psychiatric Press, 1986, pp 73–88

Waldinger RJ, Gunderson JG: Effective Psychotherapy with Borderline Patients. New York, Macmillan, 1987

Waters E, Wippman J, Stroufe LA: Attachment, positive affect and competence in the peer group: two studies in construct validation. Child Dev 50:821–829, 1979

Weissman MM, Myers JK, Ross CE (eds): Community Surveys of Psychiatric Disorders. New Brunswick, NJ, Rutgers University Press, 1986

Werner H, Kaplan B: Symbol Formation: An Organismic-Developmental Approach to Language and the Expression of Thought. New York, John Wiley, 1963

Wing JK, Bebbington P, Robins LN (eds): What Is a Case? London, Grant McIntyre, 1981

Chapter 4

Psychiatric Disorders in the Families of Borderline Outpatients

Mary C. Zanarini, Ed.D.
John G. Gunderson, M.D.
Margaret F. Marino, M.Ed.
Elizabeth O. Schwartz, M.S.
Frances R. Frankenburg, M.D.

Chapter 4

Psychiatric Disorders in the Families of Borderline Outpatients

F amily studies are an important aspect of the current research efforts to validate the borderline diagnosis (Robins and Guze 1970). If borderline personality disorder (BPD) is a valid psychiatric disorder, these efforts should reveal a heightened prevalence of BPD in the first-degree relatives of criteria-defined borderline patients. They should also reveal that the familial prevalence rate for this, and perhaps other disorders is significantly different from that of near-neighbor controls.

To date, three family history studies have been published that include BPD among the disorders systematically assessed. In the first of these studies, Loranger et al. (1982) reviewed the charts of 83 female inpatients meeting DSM-III (American Psychiatric Association 1980) criteria for BPD and found that their first-degree relatives had an 11.7% lifetime expectancy (morbid risk) of being treated for a borderline-like disorder. They also found that this morbid-risk rate was significantly higher than that found for schizophrenic or bipolar controls. The first-degree relatives of these borderline probands had a significantly higher morbid risk of being treated for major depression than did the first-degree relatives of schizophrenic controls.

In the second of these studies, Pope et al. (1983) reviewed the charts of 33 female inpatients meeting DSM-III criteria for BPD and found that only one of their 130 first-degree relatives (0.8%) met DSM-III criteria for BPD. However, they found that 10 (7.7%) of

This research was supported by the Psychosocial Research Program, McLean Hospital, Belmont, Massachusetts. This work is published with the permission of the Guilford Press and is a version of the paper "DSM-III Disorders in the Families of Borderline Outpatients" published in the *Journal of Personality Disorders*, Vol. 2, No. 4, 1988, pp. 292–302.

these relatives met DSM-III criteria for a "dramatic" cluster personality disorder, a prevalence rate significantly higher than that found in the first-degree relatives of either schizophrenic or bipolar controls. They also found that a significantly higher percentage of the first-degree relatives of the borderline probands than the first-degree relatives of the schizophrenic controls met DSM-III criteria for a major affective disorder (major depression or bipolar disorder).

In the third of these studies, Baron et al. (1985) interviewed 17 nonpatient volunteers meeting DSM-III criteria for definite ($n = 2$) or probable ($n = 15$) BPD and found that 11.7% of their first-degree relatives met DSM-III criteria for definite or probable BPD—a prevalence rate that was not significantly different from that of any of the control groups studied. However, when this prevalence rate was corrected for the lower sensitivity of the family history method compared with that of the family study method (Thompson et al. 1982), Baron and colleagues found that the resulting prevalence rate of 17.9% was significantly higher than that found for definite schizotypal and normal controls.

The study that will be described below is, to the best of our knowledge, the first family history study of outpatients that attempts to assess the familial prevalence of BPD. In addition, it improves on the design of the above-mentioned family history studies in three important ways. First, family history of psychiatric disorder was assessed blind to proband diagnosis by researchers using a semistructured interview based on DSM-III criteria. Second, the prevalence of a full range of Axis I disorders and relevant Axis II disorders was systematically assessed. Third, two rigorously diagnosed groups of personality-disordered patients who were purported to share either the impulsiveness or the chronic dysphoria of borderline patients were used as controls.

METHODS

All subjects were outpatients being treated at one of three clinics in the metropolitan Boston area (Revere Community Counseling Center, East Boston/Winthrop Community Counseling Center, and Bunker Hill Health Center in Charlestown). All patients at these facilities were considered eligible for inclusion if they were between the ages of 18 and 40 years; had normal or better intelligence; had no history of or current symptomatology of a major psychotic disorder (i.e., schizophrenia or bipolar disorder) or clear-cut organic condition; and were given a definite clinical diagnosis by the referring clinician of BPD, antisocial personality disorder (APD), or any other type of Axis II disorder as long as the person also suffered from a concomitant dysthymic disorder.

Potential subjects were referred to the study by their therapists. At the initial meeting, one of us obtained written informed consent and then evaluated the phenomenological status of each subject, blind to his or her clinical diagnosis, by administering the following three research instruments: 1) the Revised Diagnostic Interview for Borderlines (DIB-R)—a semistructured interview that can reliably distinguish clinically diagnosed borderline patients from those with other Axis II disorders (Zanarini et al. 1989a); 2) the Diagnostic Interview for Personality Disorders (DIPD)—a semistructured interview that reliably assesses the presence of the 11 Axis II disorders described in DSM-III (Zanarini et al. 1987); and 3) a draft version of the Structured Clinical Interview for DSM-III (SCID)—a structured interview designed to assess both the current and lifetime prevalance of many of the most common Axis I disorders found in DSM-III (Spitzer and Williams 1984).

Subjects who met both DIB and DSM-III criteria for BPD as assessed by the DIB-R and the DIPD were included in the borderline group. Subjects who did not meet study criteria for BPD but who met DSM-III criteria for APD as assessed by the DIPD were included in the antisocial group. The dysthymic other personality disorder (DOPD) group was composed of those subjects who did not meet the study criteria for either BPD or APD but who met the DSM-III criteria for dysthymic disorder as assessed by the SCID and who met the DSM-III criteria for some other type of Axis II disorder as assessed by the DIPD.

Family history of psychiatric disorder was assessed at a second meeting by one of two other investigators, blind to all phenomenological information, using the Family History Questionnaire (FHQ)—a two-part, semistructured interview specifically devised for this study. The first part of this instrument assesses the number of a subject's first-degree relatives who are 18 years of age or older. The second part of the instrument, which was adapted from the SCID and relevant sections of the DIPD, assesses the lifetime prevalence of 18 Axis I disorders and of borderline and antisocial personality disorders. Diagnoses were made rigorously using the full DSM-III criteria set and scoring algorithm for each disorder. The prevalence rate of all 20 disorders and the morbid-risk rate of eight selected disorders were then calculated. Morbid risk was calculated using the Weinburg short method (Slater and Cowie 1971). Relatives who had not entered the risk period were excluded, relatives within the risk period were counted as half cases, and relatives who had completed the risk period were counted as whole cases. The morbid-risk periods, which were adapted from those used by Loranger and his colleagues (Loranger et al. 1982; Loranger and Tulis 1985), were as follows: major depression (15–70); bipolar disorder (15–60); schizophrenia (15–45); and dysthymic disorder, alcohol abuse/dependence, drug abuse/dependence, BPD, and APD (15–40).

Between-group comparisons involving categorical data were computed using the χ^2 statistic corrected for continuity. Between-group comparisons involving continuous data were computed using an analysis of variance and the Newman-Keuls post hoc test of pair-wise comparisons.

RESULTS

The demographic characteristics of the resulting sample of 103 subjects can be seen in Table 4-1. The 48 borderline subjects were significantly older than the 29 antisocial subjects. They also came from

Table 4-1.   Demographic characteristics

Characteristic	BPD	APD	DOPD
Number of subjects	48	29	26
Age			
Mean	29.3	25.2*	31.3
SD	6.4	6.1	7.2
Sex (%)			
Female	66.7	27.6**	84.6
Male	33.3	72.4	15.4
Race (%)			
White	97.9	96.6	100.0
Nonwhite	2.1	3.4	0.0
Marital status (%)			
Ever married	43.8	24.1	65.4
Never married	56.2	75.9	34.6
Socioeconomic status (%)			
(I = highest, V = lowest)			
I/II	0.0	0.0	3.8**
III	10.4	10.4	26.9
IV	27.1	44.8	46.2
V	62.5	44.8	23.1

Note.   All significant comparisons in this and subsequent tables are between the borderline (BPD) group and the asterisked control group to the right: antisocial (APD) or dysthymic other personality disorder (DOPD).

*$P < .05$ (ANOVA/Newman-Keuls). **$P < .01$ (corrected χ^2 analysis).

a significantly lower socioeconomic background than the 26 DOPD controls. Borderline subjects, almost all of whom were white and who were about as likely to have been married as not, did not differ significantly from either control group on the variables of race and marital status. However, the borderline group, as expected, contained a significantly higher percentage of female subjects (66.7%) than the antisocial group (27.6%).

Overall, family history data were gathered on 488 first-degree relatives: BPD (n = 240), APD (n = 139), and DOPD (n = 109). There were no significant between-group differences in the sex distribution of relatives, as about half of the relatives in each group were female: BPD, 46.3%; APD, 51.1%; and DOPD, 57.8%. However, there was a trend indicating that a smaller percentage of the first-degree relatives of the borderline patients than the first-degree relatives of the DOPD controls were female.

Table 4-2 shows the percentage of first-degree relatives of the probands in each study group who had ever met DSM-III criteria for the Axis I and Axis II disorders assessed by the FHQ. As can be seen, nearly 25% of the relatives of the borderline subjects met criteria for an affective disorder, a substance use disorder, and one of the "dramatic" cluster personality disorders studied. In addition, about 9% of the relatives of these probands met criteria for an anxiety disorder, less than 2% met criteria for a somatoform or eating disorder, and none met criteria for a psychotic disorder. In terms of specific disorders, 16% to 18% of these relatives met criteria for major depression, alcohol abuse/dependence, and BPD. In addition, 8% to 10% met criteria for dysthymic disorder, drug abuse/dependence, and APD.

When compared with the first-degree relatives of those in each control group, a significantly higher percentage of the relatives of the borderline patients than the relatives of the antisocial controls met criteria for an affective disorder, and more specifically, dysthymic disorder. They were also significantly more likely than the relatives of those in either control group to have met criteria for BPD. In addition, a significantly higher percentage of the relatives of the borderline patients than the relatives of the DOPD controls met criteria for at least one of the "dramatic" cluster personality disorders studied. There was also a trend indicating that they were more likely than the relatives of the antisocial controls to have met criteria for major depression.

APD was 50% more common among the relatives of the antisocial controls than among the relatives of the borderline patients, a difference that did not reach statistical significance. However, when only the psychiatrically disordered relatives of each group of probands were considered (BPD = 119, APD = 59, DOPD = 54), a significantly higher percentage of the disordered relatives of the antisocial subjects (35.6%) than of the borderline patients (20.2%) met criteria for APD ($P < .05$).

Table 4-2. Prevalence of DSM-III disorders in first-degree relatives

DSM-III disorder	BPD (%)	APD (%)	DOPD (%)
Affective disorders	23.3	11.5***	30.3
Major depression	15.8	8.6*	22.0
Dysthymic disorder	10.0	3.6**	11.1
Bipolar disorder	0.4	0.7	0.9
Cyclothymic disorder	0.4	0.0	0.0
Substance use disorders	23.3	25.2	22.0
Alcohol abuse/dependence	17.9	19.4	20.2
Drug abuse/dependence	7.9	8.6	5.5
Psychotic disorders	0.0	1.4	0.0
Schizophrenia	0.0	1.4	0.0
Other psychotic disorder	0.0	0.0	0.0
Anxiety disorders	8.8	6.5	10.1
Panic disorder	0.8	0.7	2.8
Agoraphobia	3.8	0.7	4.6
Social/simple phobia	4.2	3.6	4.6
Obsessive-compulsive disorder	0.0	0.0	0.0
Generalized anxiety disorder	0.4	1.4	0.0
Somatoform disorders	1.3	2.2	0.9
Somatization disorder	0.4	0.7	0.0
Hypochondriasis	0.8	1.4	0.9
Eating disorders	1.3	2.9	0.0
Anorexia	0.8	0.0	0.0
Bulimia	0.4	2.9	0.0
Personality disorders	22.5	16.6	11.9**
Borderline personality disorder	18.3	2.9****	7.3**
Antisocial personality disorder	10.0	15.1	7.3

*$P < .1$. **$P < .05$. ***$P < .01$. ****$P < .001$. (Corrected χ^2 analysis).

Table 4-3 shows the morbid risk of developing eight of the disorders discussed above. The number of relatives at risk for each disorder is as follows: major depression—BPD = 122, APD = 70, DOPD = 56; bipolar disorder—BPD = 135, APD = 76, DOPD = 68; schizophrenia—BPD = 166, APD = 91, DOPD = 78; and the two substance use and the two personality disorders—BPD = 177, APD = 98, DOPD = 83. As can be seen, the lifetime expectancy of a first-degree relative of a borderline proband developing each of the nonschizophrenic disorders was anywhere from 35% to 98% higher than the prevalence rate for the same disorder, the morbid risk of BPD being 36% higher than the prevalence rate for BPD. However, between-group comparisons revealed exactly the same relationships as were found for prevalence rates; BPD, major depression, and dysthymic disorder were the only disorders that had a morbid risk that discriminated the relatives of borderline patients from the relatives of controls at the trend level or better.

Table 4-4 shows the prevalence rates of affective disorders among the first-degree relatives of the borderline patients who had a lifetime history of major depression ($n = 37$), the borderline patients without such a history ($n = 11$), and controls. As can be seen, a significantly higher percentage of the relatives of the depressed borderline patients ($n = 187$) than the relatives of the "pure" borderline patients ($n = 53$) met criteria for an affective disorder, and more specifically, major depression. They were also significantly more likely than the relatives of antisocial controls to have met criteria for an affective disorder, and more specifically, major depression and dysthymic disorder. However, the relatives of the "pure" borderline patients were significantly less

Table 4-3. Morbid risk of selected DSM-III disorders in first-degree relatives

DSM-III disorder	BPD (%)	APD (%)	DOPD (%)
Major depression	31.2	17.1*	42.9
Dysthymic disorder	13.6	5.1**	14.5
Bipolar disorder	0.7	1.3	1.5
Schizophrenia	0.0	2.2	0.0
Alcohol abuse/dependence	24.3	27.6	26.5
Drug abuse/dependence	10.7	12.2	7.2
Borderline personality disorder	24.9	4.1	9.6***
Antisocial personality disorder	13.6	21.4	9.6

*$P < .1$. **$P < .05$. ***$P < .01$. ****$P < .001$. (Corrected χ^2 analysis).

likely than the relatives of the DOPD controls to have met criteria for an affective disorder, and more specifically, major depression.

DISCUSSION

Borderline Personality Disorder

About 18% of the first-degree relatives of the borderline subjects in this study met DSM-III criteria for BPD, and the morbid-risk rate for this disorder was found to be about 25%. Although BPD was not uncommon in the families of controls, particularly DOPD controls, these rates were significantly higher than those found in either control group. They are also higher than the comparable figures found in the three prior family history studies that have assessed this area of Axis II pathology. Specifically, the 18.3% prevalence rate found in this study is much higher than the 0.8% prevalence rate found by Pope et al. (1983). This difference may be due to the fact that these investigators were trying to make rigorous DSM-III diagnoses based on the somewhat sketchy, highly variable information contained in the inpatient charts of their borderline cohort. The 24.9% morbid-risk rate for DSM-III BPD found in this study is also considerably higher than the 11.7% morbid-risk rate for a borderline-like disorder found by Loranger et al. (1982). This difference is not surprising, as Loranger and colleagues' results pertained only to first-degree relatives who had been treated for such a disorder, and only 21% of the relatives of their borderline cohort had a history of psychiatric treatment. The 18.3% prevalence rate for DSM-III BPD found in this study is also somewhat higher than the 11.7% prevalence rate for

Table 4-4. Prevalence of affective disorders in first-degree relatives of depressed borderline, "pure" borderline, and control subjects

DSM-III disorder	Depressed BPD (%)	Pure BPD (%)	APD (%)	DOPD (%)
Affective disorder	27.8	7.6**	11.5***	30.3†
Major depression	19.8	1.9**	8.6**	22.0†
Dysthymic disorder	11.2	5.7	3.6*	11.1
Bipolar disorder	0.5	0.0	0.7	0.9
Cyclothymic disorder	0.5	0.0	0.0	0.0

*$P < .05$, depressed BPD vs. APD (corrected χ^2 analysis); **$P < .01$, depressed BPD vs. pure BPD and APD (corrected χ^2 analysis); ***$P < .001$, depressed BPD vs. APD; †$P < .01$, pure BPD vs. DOPD (corrected χ^2 analysis).

definite and probable BPD found by Baron et al. (1985). This difference is also not surprising, as their results pertained to the first-degree relatives of 17 general population volunteers, 15 of whom exhibited only borderline traits. However, it should be noted that their corrected prevalence rate of 17.9% is almost identical to the 18.3% prevalence rate found in the current study.

Taken together, the results of this study are consistent with the heightened familial prevalence of BPD-like disorders found by Loranger et al. and Baron et al. However, these results extend the findings of these earlier studies by suggesting that the familial prevalence of this disorder, even when rigorously diagnosed by DSM-III criteria, may be somewhat higher than previously estimated. They also extend the results of these studies, which found that BPD was more common in the families of borderline probands than in the families of schizophrenic, bipolar, schizotypal, and normal controls, by indicating that BPD is significantly more common in the families of borderline probands than in the families of two very near-neighbor groups of personality-disordered outpatients.

Antisocial Personality Disorder

Ten percent of the first-degree relatives of the borderline subjects in this study and about 20% of the impaired first-degree relatives of these probands met DSM-III criteria for APD. Although these rates are high, antisocial controls were significantly more likely than borderline probands to have an impaired first-degree relative who met DSM-III criteria for APD. Pope et al. (1983) and Soloff and Millward (1983b) have also found a heightened familial prevalence of APD among borderline probands. However, the percentage of first-degree relatives in this study who met criteria for APD is slightly higher than the 6.2% to 6.9% found by these investigators. These differences may be due to the semistructured interview method used in the current study. This method assessed the prevalence of antisocial behaviors in a more uniform and thorough manner than the chart reviews and/or unstructured clinical interviews used in the other studies.

In sum, the results of this study suggest a somewhat closer familial relationship between BPD and APD than that found in prior studies. However, they also suggest that each disorder is significantly more common in the families of similarly affected probands than in the families of controls with the other disorder. This contradicts Pope et al.'s contention that these disorders, in conjunction with the other "dramatic" cluster disorders (histrionic and narcissistic personality disorders), may function as a single category.

Affective Disorders

About 25% of the first-degree relatives of the borderline subjects in this study met DSM-III criteria for an affective disorder. About 16% met criteria for major depression, 10% met criteria for dysthymic disorder, and less than 1% met criteria for either bipolar or cyclothymic disorder. These rates were very similar to those of the DOPD controls. However, a significantly higher percentage of the relatives of the borderline probands than the relatives of the antisocial controls met criteria for an affective disorder, and more specifically, dysthymic disorder. There was also a trend indicating that these relatives were more likely than the relatives of the antisocial controls to have met criteria for major depression.

The results of this study are consistent with those of other family history studies that have found a heightened prevalence of major depression among the first-degree relatives of criteria-defined borderline patients (Akiskal et al. 1985; Andrulonis and Vogel 1984; Baron et al. 1985; Loranger et al. 1982; Pope et al. 1983; Soloff and Millward 1983b). Prevalence rates in these studies ranged from 4.6% to 17%, and morbid-risk rates ranged from 6.4% to 13.3%. They are also consistent with the results of family history studies that have found a very low prevalence of bipolar disorder among the first-degree relatives of criteria-defined borderline patients (Loranger et al. 1982; Pope et al. 1983). However, the 0.4% prevalence rate for bipolar disorder found in this study is much lower than the 17% found by Akiskal et al. (1985). This difference may be explained by the fact that about 25% of Akiskal et al.'s borderline probands met criteria for a concomitant bipolar II or cyclothymic disorder.

When viewed from a different vantage point, the between-group differences observed in this study seem strongly associated with the affective histories of the borderline probands. The relatives of the borderline patients with a history of major depression were significantly more likely than the relatives of the "pure" borderline patients and the antisocial controls to have met criteria for major depression. In contrast, the relatives of the "pure" borderline patients were affectively very similar to the relatives of the antisocial controls, but were significantly less likely than the relatives of the DOPD controls to have met criteria for major depression. This constitutes a series of findings concerning the effect of coexisting proband depressions on familial rates of affective disorder that are consistent with those reported by Pope et al. (1983).

Taken together, the results of this study suggest that the familial link between BPD and unipolar affective disorder may be less specific than has sometimes been contended (Akiskal 1981; Klein 1975; Stone 1979), as all three study groups exhibited relatively high rates of major depression and dysthymic disorder. The results of this study also suggest that the heightened prevalence of affective disorder found among the relatives of these borderline probands may be largely accounted for by the high percentage of these probands with a personal history of major depression.

Substance Use Disorders

About 25% of the first-degree relatives of the borderline subjects in this study met DSM-III criteria for a substance use disorder. Alcohol abuse/dependence was about twice as common as drug abuse/dependence. However, borderline patients were not successfully discriminated from controls on this variable, as substance use disorders were about equally common in the families of all three study groups. Each of the other studies that have investigated this area of familial psychopathology has also found that substance use disorders were common in the first-degree relatives of criteria-defined borderline patients (Andrulonis and Vogel 1984; Baron et al 1985; Loranger and Tulis 1985; Pope et al. 1983; Soloff and Millward 1983b). All of these studies, except that of Loranger and Tulis (1985), have also found that the familial rates of substance use disorders observed in the first-degree relatives of borderline probands cannot be distinguished from those found in the families of controls, regardless of whether schizophrenic, affectively disordered, schizotypal, or normal controls were studied.

In sum, the results of this study are consistent with those of earlier studies that found that both alcohol and drug abuse are common disorders in the first-degree relatives of borderline probands. However, they extend the results of all but one of these earlier studies by suggesting that the familial prevalence rates of substance use disorders are essentially similar for borderline probands and two groups of seriously personality-disordered controls.

Schizophrenia

None of the borderline probands in this study had a first-degree relative who met DSM-III criteria for schizophrenia. However, the family history of borderline probands could not be distinguished from that of controls on this variable, as only two control subjects had a first-degree relative who met criteria for this disorder. The absence of schizophrenia in this study is consistent with the results of most other family history studies, which have found little or no schizophrenia in the first-degree relatives of criteria-defined borderline patients (Akiskal et al. 1985; Andrulonis and Vogel 1984; Loranger et al. 1982; Pope et al. 1983; Soloff and Millward 1983b; Stone 1979; Stone et al. 1981). However, it is at variance with the 11% prevalence rate found by Stone (1977) in the first of his three family history studies. This difference may be due, as Stone has suggested, to the fact that many of these borderline outpatients were actually socially isolated schizoid or schizotypal characters without a history of suicidality or deliberately self-destructive behaviors. In summary, the results of this study combine with those of most earlier family history studies to suggest that there is little, if any, familial link between BPD and DSM-III schizophrenia.

CONCLUSIONS

The family history of 48 borderline, 29 antisocial, and 26 DOPD outpatients was assessed using a semistructured interview based on DSM-III criteria. Five important findings emerge from the results of this study. First, BPD was found to be somewhat more common in the families of borderline probands than previously estimated. It was also found to be significantly more common in these families than in the families of two groups of near-neighbor personality-disordered controls. Taken together, these findings seem to suggest that BPD, like other valid disorders, "breeds true." Second, the familial prevalence rates for affective disorder, and more specifically, dysthymic disorder, were significantly higher for borderline probands than antisocial but not DOPD controls. However, the relatively high prevalence rates found in both control groups seem to indicate that the familial link between BPD and unipolar depressions is more nonspecific than previously suggested. In addition, the heightened prevalence of affective disorder found among the relatives of borderline probands seems largely attributable to a coexisting affective disorder in about 75% of these probands. Third, APD, although common in the families of borderline probands, was significantly more common among the impaired relatives of antisocial controls. This finding, in conjunction with the other findings of this study, seems to suggest that BPD and APD are separate, albeit very near-neighbor, Axis II disorders. Fourth, both alcohol abuse and drug abuse were found to be common but nondiscriminating disorders in the families of borderline patients. Fifth, schizophrenia was absent from the families of borderline probands, suggesting that little, if any, relationship exists between these two disorders.

Comment

The results of this study lend further support to the view that BPD is a valid psychiatric disorder. However, the etiological significance of this and other family history studies remains unclear. It may be that borderline patients inherit a genetic predisposition to develop the traits that define the disorder (i.e., affective lability; disturbed but generally nonpsychotic ideation; impulsivity, particularly of a self-destructive nature; and intense, unstable relationships). It may also be that BPD develops in response to certain childhood events that may or may not be associated with particular forms of familial or, more specifically, parental psychopathology. Finally, and perhaps most likely, it may be that there is both a genetic and an environmental component to the etiology of BPD. In this view, both the genetic predisposition to develop symptom patterns characteristic of BPD and the precipitating influence of certain environmentally mediated factors would be necessary to develop a full-blown borderline syndrome.

The empirical evidence for each of these hypotheses varies greatly. Studies involving the more methodologically rigorous family study method, which involves directly interviewing all available and/or willing first-degree relatives, are needed to confirm the results of the family history studies described above, which obtained information from indirect sources (e.g., the probands, inpatient charts). However, only twin and adoption studies can determine whether there is a genetic component to the etiology of BPD and, if so, the strength or potency of this component. To date, no adoption studies of criteria-defined borderline patients or their offspring have been conducted. In the only twin study that has been published, Torgersen (1984) found that none of the 3 monozygotic co-twins but 2 of the 7 dizygotic co-twins of 10 criteria-defined borderline probands were concordant for BPD. From these results, Torgersen concluded that genetic factors did not seem to influence the development of BPD.

Ultimately, prospective studies of at-risk populations will be necessary to determine the environmental factors that are implicated in the development of BPD. However, numerous retrospective studies of the childhood experiences of criteria-defined borderline patients have already been conducted. In the first generation of these studies, parental overinvolvement, emotional neglect, and negative conflictual relationships were all found to be characteristic of the childhood histories of these patients (Frank and Hoffman 1986; Frank and Paris 1981; Goldberg et al. 1985; Grinker et al. 1968; Gunderson et al. 1980; Soloff and Millward 1983a; Walsh 1977). In addition, a childhood history involving lengthy separations from or the permanent loss of such adults was found to discriminate borderline patients from schizophrenic, depressed, and personality-disordered controls (Akiskal et al 1985; Bradley 1979; Soloff and Millward 1983a; Walsh 1977).

More recently, a second generation of methodologically more rigorous studies has begun to appear (Links et al. 1988; Zanarini et al. 1989b). These studies have confirmed the high prevalence of early childhood separations found in earlier studies. However, they have also found that about a quarter of their borderline cohorts reported a childhood history of sexual abuse, and somewhere between 29% and 46% reported a childhood history of physical abuse. In addition, both of these studies have found that borderline patients were significantly more likely to report having a history of sexual abuse than near-neighbor Axis II controls. Zanarini et al. also found that 72% of their borderline cohort reported having been victims of prolonged, repetitive verbal abuse, a finding that strongly discriminated these patients from the Axis II controls studied.

What relationship, if any, exists between these forms of mistreatment at the hands of caregivers and specific forms of psychopathology manifested by these caregivers is as yet unknown. Currently, we are engaged in such a study and hope that it will shed light on the types of caregiver psychopathology that are most closely associated with these forms of caregiver dyscontrol. It may be that the day-to-day presence of an erratic but nonabusive parent may be equally important in the etiology of BPD. Studies that address this issue are needed. However, clinical experience suggests that the environmental factors associated with the etiology of BPD are particularly complex and that no one factor, however traumatic, is in itself necessary or sufficient for the development of the disorder.

REFERENCES

Akiskal HS: Subaffective disorders: dysthymic, cyclothymic and bipolar II disorders in the "borderline" realm. Psychiatr Clin North Am 4:25–46, 1981

Akiskal HS, Chen SE, Davis GC, et al: Borderline: an adjective in search of a noun. J Clin Psychiatry 46:41–48, 1985

American Psychiatric Association: Diagnostic and Statistical Manual of Mental Disorders, 3rd Edition. Washington, DC, American Psychiatric Association, 1980

Andrulonis PA, Vogel NG: Comparison of borderline personality subcategories to schizophrenic and affective disorders. Br J Psychiatry 144:358–363, 1984

Baron M, Gruen R, Asnis L, et al: Familial transmission of schizotypal and BPDs. Am J Psychiatry 142:927–933, 1985

Bradley SJ: The relationship of early mental separation to borderline personality in children and adolescents: a pilot study. Am J Psychiatry 136:424–426, 1979

Frank H, Hoffman N: Borderline empathy: an empirical investigation. Compr Psychiatry 27:387–395, 1986

Frank H, Paris J: Recollections of family experience in borderline patients. Arch Gen Psychiatry 38:1031–1034, 1981

Goldberg RL, Mann LS, Wise TN, et al: Parental qualities as perceived by borderline personality disorders. Hillside J Clin Psychiatry 7:134–140, 1985

Grinker RR, Werble B, Drye RC: The Borderline Syndrome. New York, Basic Books, 1968

Gunderson JG, Kerr J, Englund DW: The families of borderlines: a comparative study. Arch Gen Psychiatry 37:27–33, 1980

Klein DF: Psychopharmacology and the borderline patient, in Borderline States in Psychiatry. Edited by Mack J. New York, Grune & Stratton, 1975, pp 75–91

Links PS, Steiner M, Offord D, et al: Characteristics of borderline personality disorder: a Canadian study. Can J Psychiatry 33:336–340, 1988

Loranger AW, Tulis EH: Family history of alcoholism in borderline personality disorder. Arch Gen Psychiatry 42:153–157, 1985

Loranger AW, Oldham JM, Tulis EH: Familial transmission of DSM-III borderline personality disorder. Arch Gen Psychiatry 39:795–799, 1982

Pope HG, Jonas JM, Hudson JI, et al: The validity of DSM-III borderline personality disorder. Arch Gen Psychiatry 40:23–30, 1983

Robins E, Guze SB: Establishment of diagnostic validity in psychiatric illness: its application to schizophrenia. Am J Psychiatry 126:983–987, 1970

Slater E, Cowie V: The Genetics of Mental Disorders. London, Oxford University Press, 1971

Soloff PH, Millward JW: Developmental histories of borderline patients. Compr Psychiatry 24:574–588, 1983a

Soloff PH, Millward JW: Psychiatric disorders in the families of borderline patients. Arch Gen Psychiatry 40:37–44, 1983b

Spitzer RL, Williams JBW: Structured Clinical Interview for DSM-III. New York, New York State Psychiatric Institute, 1984

Stone MH: The borderline syndrome: evolution of the term, genetic aspects, and prognosis. Am J Psychother 31:345–365, 1977

Stone MH: Contemporary shift of the borderline concept from a sub-schizophrenic disorder to a subaffective disorder. Psychiatr Clin North Am 2:577–594, 1979

Stone MH, Kahn E, Flye B: Psychiatrically ill relatives of borderline patients. Psychiatr Q 53:71–84, 1981

Thompson WD, Orvaschel H, Prusoff BA, et al: An evaluation of the family history method for ascertaining psychiatric disorders. Arch Gen Psychiatry 39:53–58, 1982

Torgersen S: Genetic and nosological aspects of schizotypal and borderline personality disorders. Arch Gen Psychiatry 41:546–554, 1984

Walsh F: Family study 1976: fourteen new borderline cases, in The Borderline Patient. Edited by Grinker RR, Werble B. New York, Jason Aronson, 1977, pp 158–177

Zanarini MC, Frankenburg FR, Chauncey DL, et al: The diagnostic interview for personality disorders: interrater and test-retest reliability. Compr Psychiatry 28:467–480, 1987

Zanarini MC, Gunderson JG, Frankenburg FR, et al: The revised diagnostic interview for borderlines: discriminating BPD from other Axis II disorders. Journal of Personality Disorders 3:10–18, 1989a

Zanarini MC, Gunderson JG, Marino MF, et al: Childhood experiences of borderline patients. Compr Psychiatry 30:18–25, 1989b

Chapter 5

The Childhood Experience of the Borderline Patient

Susan N. Ogata, Ph.D.
Kenneth R. Silk, M.D.
Sonya Goodrich, Ph.D.

Chapter 5

The Childhood Experience of the Borderline Patient

There have been few systematic assessments of the borderline patient's early psychosocial experiences. Despite great theoretical interest in the psychodynamics of borderline patients (Gunderson and Englund 1981; Kernberg 1975; Masterson 1976), little empirical research in the area of childhood experiences or events has taken place. Family investigations, primarily theoretical in orientation, attempt to describe family constellations based on purely clinical data. The few studies that do exist, regardless of their methodology, present conflicting results.

Much has been written concerning the psychological development of the borderline patient (e.g., Kernberg 1975; Masterson 1972). Psychoanalytic theories suggest that developmental failure during the rapprochement subphase of separation-individuation eventually culminates in the maladaptive defenses and poor ego integration that manifest as borderline psychopathology during late adolescence and early adulthood (Mahler et al. 1975; Masterson 1972, 1976). However, Gunderson (1984) questions how a specific or single developmental failure or trauma can eventually lead in adulthood to a disorder that has multiple defects and symptoms in many areas of functioning. By implication, Gunderson suggests that familial-environmental factors, deficits, or traumas that are repetitive or persist over long periods of time during childhood may be more important in the eventual development of borderline pathology than a single developmental event. For example, previous studies comparing affective patients with and without borderline personality disorder (BPD) or traits suggest that borderline patients have more difficulty in both elementary and high school than their nonborderline affective comparison groups (Charney et al. 1981; Gaviria et al. 1982). However, these studies did not systematically explore the specific events, stressors, or traumata their subjects had experienced during childhood and adolescence that may have contributed to their poor adaptation.

Although the clinical literature repeatedly emphasizes issues of separation and loss as being significant in the early development of the future borderline patient (Gunderson and Englund 1981), these ideas have rarely been empirically tested. The few studies that have addressed these issues typically make no specifications about the frequency or duration of loss or separation experiences, or provide only a narrow range of such events. Neither is there consistency across studies as to the type of events assessed, rendering it difficult to make generalizable conclusions.

Bradley (1979) assessed separation experiences in a group of 14 borderline children and adolescents defined by Gunderson and Singer's (1975) criteria. Separation experiences were defined as either removal of the child or extended maternal or caregiver absence (greater than 4 weeks). Bradley found that there were significantly more separation experiences in the borderline cohort during the first 5 years of the patient's life when compared with nonborderline psychiatric patients or delinquent nonpsychiatric controls. However, there was no difference between groups for separation experiences during the period when the subjects were ages 6 to 10 years.

Soloff and Millward (1983) compared developmental, i.e., psychosocial and neurological, histories of 45 borderline patients who were identified by the Diagnostic Interview for Borderlines (DIB) (Gunderson et al. 1981), 32 depressed patients, and 42 schizophrenic inpatients. Although their results failed to find increased neuro-developmental deficits among the borderline patients when compared with the control groups, they did find that the borderline group had more difficulty than the schizophrenic group, and particularly more than the depressive group, in their reactions to certain separation events such as entering elementary school, going to high school, and leaving the parental home. They found significantly fewer intact families among the borderline patients, and an increased incidence of parental marital separation and divorce, occurring before the subjects were 6 years old, that resulted in loss of a parent, particularly the father.

Greenman et al. (1986), however, failed to find significant differences in rates of parental separation and divorce when they retrospectively diagnosed and compared 27 borderline inpatient children with 59 nonborderline inpatient children. In this study, more than 40% of all the subjects came from families in which the parents were either separated or divorced, a figure similar to the borderline but not the depressed or schizophrenic cohorts in the Soloff and Millward (1983) study. The relationship between parental separation and divorce and psychiatric hospitalization among children is an interesting finding, but further exploration is beyond the scope of this chapter.

In a recent study comparing developmental histories of 27 DIB-diagnosed, inpatient borderline adolescents with 23 inpatient psychiatric, nonborderline adolescent controls (P. S. Ludolph et al. 1988, personal communication), borderline patients had significantly more disrupted attachments throughout childhood, but not specifically before the age of 5, contrary to the results found by Bradley (1979). Borderline patients had significantly more separations or overt rejections from their primary caregiver, significantly more maternal or paternal surrogates, and a greater history of adoption. Thus, there appears to be some discrepancy between studies regarding the rate of particular separation events in the borderline patient's history. Moreover, there is no inclusion of other experiences that fall under the umbrella of loss and separation, for example, death of siblings or other close relatives and significant others, or recurrent lengthy separations from the mother or father.

Other childhood experiences significant in the development of borderline psychopathology but not thoroughly or empirically addressed in the literature are sexual abuse and physical abuse. No systematic studies have been published to date that evaluate the frequency and impact of such early traumatic events in the borderline group (Ogata et al. 1988). Several authors have suggested that such events may play crucial roles in the development of future borderline psychopathology, particularly the relationship instability, the sense of ego fragmentation, and the ineffective ways of coping with interpersonal conflict (Brooks 1982; Herman and van der Kolk 1987; Stone 1981). Herman and van der Kolk (1987) suggest that posttraumatic symptoms in general, and of severely abused individuals in particular, resemble the symptoms often seen in patients with BPD. However, most of these authors are typically not specific about the type of abuse, refer exclusively to incestuous abuse, and ignore the role played by extrafamilial abuse.

Finally, other stressful childhood events, for example, changes of primary caregivers, serious physical or psychiatric illness of a parent, or significant social and academic problems in school, have never been systematically evaluated with a borderline proband. The repetitive or ongoing influence of such experiences may prove to be important differentiating developmental factors.

In this study, we attempt to identify systematically the type and frequency of early stressful, and possibly traumatic, familial events and the family environment of borderline patients, comparing their experiences with a nonborderline, depressed group. We chose a depressed group of subjects because this psychiatric comparison allowed us to address the current controversy over the interface between borderline and affective disorders (Akiskal et al. 1985; Gunderson and Elliot 1985; Kroll and Ogata 1987). The study addresses the following questions:

- Do borderline patients experience a greater frequency of a variety of separation- and loss-related events than do depressive patients?
- Do borderline patients experience a greater frequency of stressful, abusive, and traumatic events than do depressive patients?
- Are the family environments of borderline patients more unstable than those of depressive patients, featuring greater conflict and disorganization, and less cohesion and personal growth?
- Do borderline patients recall their families as more problematic during their adolescent years, when issues of separation-individuation are speculated to become magnified for the family, than during the childhood period, as compared with depressive patients?

METHODS

All subjects were drawn from two inpatient units at the University of Michigan Medical Center. They comprised male and female inpatients between the ages of 18 and 60 years. A total of 42 patients participated in the study, including 24 borderline and 18 depressive patients. Subjects included in this study were those who agreed to participate in the ongoing research project studying the relationship between BPD and affective disorders conducted at the University of Michigan Medical Center in Ann Arbor.

Patients satisfying at least two DSM-III (American Psychiatric Association 1980) criteria for BPD or schizotypal personality disorder or three DSM-III criteria for major depressive disorder (MDD) were considered potential subjects. The 91% of eligible subjects who agreed to participate in the study were first evaluated by a staff psychologist or psychiatrist with the DIB. This group has had high interrater reliability on the DIB, with a Pearson correlation of .78 (Cornell et al. 1981), and reliability has been maintained through frequent retrainings.

Subjects who obtained a score of 7 or higher were included in the borderline group. It was decided in advance to exclude subjects scoring 6 on the DIB to minimize group overlap. Those who scored 5 or less on the DIB were considered potential nonborderline affective-disordered subjects.

Patients qualified for the depressive group if, in addition to a DIB score of 5 or less, they met the Research Diagnostic Criteria (RDC) (Spitzer et al. 1978) for probable or definite MDD. A consensus RDC diagnosis was made by diagnosticians consisting of the subject's primary therapist and the senior supervisor, both of whom were blind to the DIB results. Senior supervisors achieved an average interrater reliability on the RDC diagnosis of depression of .92 (weighted kappa) (Cohen 1968), with a range of pairwise reliability of .88 to .94. Exclusion criteria for the study included organic disorders, chronic psychosis, medical illness that would confound certain biological tests, age over 60, nonnative English speaking, and IQ below 65.

After a week of hospitalization, or when the patient was out of the initial crisis stage as determined by the primary therapist, an interview was conducted by the first author or an advanced clinical psychology graduate student to assess the frequency, severity, duration, emotional impact, and age of occurrence of a variety of early family events with the Familial Experiences Interview (FEI). This interview schedule was developed by Dr. Ogata in collaboration with the members of the research team. This 40-category, semistructured interview taps areas of family experiences related to loss, separation, psychiatric disorder of parents, abuse, and other disruptive events before the age of 18, as recalled by the subject. The items were drawn from the borderline and depressive literature regarding early developmental experiences, from the life events literature, and from subjects' reports of their own early experiences during the piloting of the interview. Table 5-1 shows an outline of the categories and respective events that were explored with the subject during the interview. Reliability of the entire interview, using kappa coefficients, ranged from .47 to 1.0. Reliability for all items that indicated occurrence of an event ranged from .75 to 1.0. Most of the items with reliability below .80 attempted to determine impact, severity, and subject age for an event. Out of 159 total items, only 6 received a reliability of .70 and below on the interview.

Subsequent to the interview, subjects were asked to complete the Family Environment Scale (FES) (Moos and Moos 1981). This self-report measure consists of 90 true-false items and assesses the social environmental characteristics of families. The 10 FES subscales are grouped into three underlying dimensions: 1) relationships, 2) personal growth, and 3) system maintenance. The FES was developed with the assumption that the family environment can have a unique personality that can be measured in the same way that individual personality measurements are made. Reliability studies demonstrated internal consistencies that ranged from .61 to .78 for the 10 subscales. Intercorrelations indicated that these scales measured distinct but somewhat related features of family environments. Those scales that were positively correlated were cohesion and organization, and intellectual-cultural orientation and active-recreational orientation. Nega-

Table 5-1. Familial Experiences Interview (FEI) category
descriptions

Category	Description
Loss	Death of mother Death of father Death of sibling Death of close relative Death of nonclose relative Death of significant other Death of pet
Separation	Separation from one parent due to divorce Separation from both parents Frequent absences of mother Frequent absences of father Mother beginning to work Separation anxiety related to school Jail sentence of a parent
Psychiatric disorder of a parent	Mental illness of mother Mental illness of father Alcohol/drug abuse of mother Alcohol/drug abuse of father Personality disorder of mother Personality disorder of father
Abuse	Sexual abuse by father Sexual abuse by mother Sexual abuse by sibling Sexual abuse by relative Sexual abuse by nonfamily member Physical abuse by parent Physical neglect by parent

Other disruptive events	Marital discord
	Marital separation
	Divorce of parents
	Serious physical illness of subject
	Serious physical illness of parent
	Extramarital affair(s) of parent
	Significant social, academic, or authority
	    problems in school
	Change in financial status
	Change of primary caregivers
	Change in family residence
	Birth of sibling
	Long period of unemployment of primary
	    provider
	Adoption of subject

tive correlations were found between cohesion and conflict and between independence and control. Test-retest reliabilities ranged from .68 to .86 for an 8-week interval, and .52 and .89 for a 12-month interval. Subjects in this study were asked to complete the FES for two different age periods: 1) childhood, from birth to age 12, and 2) adolescence, from age 13 to 18.

RESULTS

The demographic profiles of the groups studied are shown on Table 5-2. The borderline group (mean age, 30 years) were significantly younger than the depressive group (mean age, 42 years). They were more likely to be single and to be students or have part-time employment. Depressive subjects, in contrast, were more likely to be married or divorced and to be housewives. Both groups were predominantly white and female, and had similar educational and occupational backgrounds. They also had comparable family characteristics with regard to family size and birth order.

A comparison between groups was made of the rates of loss- and separation-related events. Loss events were defined as death of mother, father, sibling, close relative, nonclose relative, significant other, and pet, as well as the death of nonbiological (i.e., step, adoptive, foster, half) family members. There were no significant differences between groups on the reporting of any loss events. Few subjects from both groups reported the death of parental figures and siblings, whereas at least 50% in both groups reported the death of close relatives, nonclose relatives, and pets.

Separation events included separation from one parent due to divorce, separation from both parents, frequent absences of mother or father, mother beginning to work, separation anxiety related to school, and jail sentence of a parent. Again, no significant differences emerged between groups on any of these indices. There was a trend for borderline subjects to report a greater frequency of separation events, but less than one-third of the subjects reported the occurrence of any of these events. The lone exception was separation from both parents for at least a 2-week period at one time during childhood; 50% of the borderline patients and almost 30% of the depressive patients reported such an event.

Borderline patients did experience a significantly higher rate of sexual abuse in their childhood years, including abuse by family members as well as nonfamily individuals, than did the depressed group. Seventy-one percent of the borderline patients but only 22% of the depressive patients reported a history of sexual abuse ($P < .01$).

Although we used a broad definition of sexual abuse, including exhibitionism and fondling, over 40% of the sexual abuse involved penetration. Physical neglect was relatively infrequent in both groups, whereas physical abuse was reported in 42% of the borderline and 33%

Table 5-2.   Descriptive characteristics of borderline and depressed subjects

Variable	Borderline $n = 24$	Depressed $n = 18$
Sex (% female)	79	72
Mean age (years)	30	42**
Marital status (%)*		
Single	63	17
Married	13	56
Separated	8	0
Divorced	13	28
Employment (%)*		
Employed	33	39
Unemployed	25	22
Student	13	0
Housewife	0	33
Part-time employment	13	0
Disabled	17	0
Education (mean number of years)	14	14
Occupation (%)		
Laborer	21	0
Clerical	13	39
Skilled craft	4	11
Manager	8	0
Professional	29	28
None of the above	25	22
Race (% white)	83	89
Religion (%)		
Catholic	25	59
Protestant	58	29
Sibship (mean no.)	3.9	3.5
Birth order (%)		
Youngest	29	33
Middle	38	33
Oldest	33	33

*$P < .01$. **$P < .001$.

of the depressive patients, a nonsignificant difference. These results have been reported in greater detail elsewhere (Ogata et al. 1988).

Exploratory analyses were conducted to assess what other disruptive childhood events recalled by subjects distinguished the groups. Significant differences emerged with six of these events, shown on Table 5-3: 1) serious mental illness of a parent, 2) substance abuse by a parent, 3) personality disorder of a parent, 4) problems with elementary school, 5) problems with high school, and 6) change of family residence.

Of the 17 borderline patients (71%) who recalled having, before the age of 18, a parent who experienced what was described as a serious mental illness (major depressive disorder, bipolar disorder, schizoaffective disorder, or schizophrenia), 12 described the mother as having an illness; 2, the father; and 3, both mother and father. Of the 9 borderline patients (38%) who recalled having a parent with a substance abuse disorder, 1 described the mother as having the disorder; 5, the father; and 3, both mother and father. Of the 18 borderline patients (75%) who recalled having a parent with a personality disorder, 8 described the mother as having the disorder; 7, the father; and 3, both mother and father.

Social problems during elementary and high school were also more frequently reported by borderline patients (19 of 24 and 24 of 24, respectively). In fact, every borderline subject reported significant difficulties during high school. Typically, these problems were of an ongoing nature and had a significant emotional impact on the subject. Subjects reported having the most difficulty relating with peers, especially during the high-school years. They frequently described

Table 5-3. Percentage of subjects experiencing disruptive childhood events

Event	Borderline $n = 24$	Depressed $n = 18$	χ^2
	%	%	
Mental illness of parent	71	33	5.84*
Substance abuse by a parent	38	11	3.71*
Personality disorder of parent	75	22	11.48**
Problems in elementary school	79	44	5.40*
Problems in high school	100	39	19.87**
Change of family residence	50	83	4.98*

*$P < .05$. **$P < .01$.

themselves as an "outsider" or a "loner," without age-appropriate relationships or social supports.

Finally, changes in family residence were significantly more frequent for the depressive group than for the borderline group. Eighty-three percent (15 of 18) of depressive patients changed their residence at least once before the age of 18, whereas only 50% (12 of 24) of the borderline patients did so.

We predicted that on the FES borderline patients would score their family higher on conflict (the amount of openly expressed anger, aggression, and conflict among family members) and lower on organization (the degree of importance of clear organization and structure in planning family activities and responsibilities) and cohesion (the degree of commitment, help, and support family members provide for one another) compared with depressive patients. The results of t-test analyses were consistent with these predictions, particularly for the adolescent period (Table 5-4). On the FES, subjects responded to the scale for two time periods: Time 1, ages 0 through 12 (childhood); Time 2, ages 13 through 18 (adolescence). For Time 1, borderline subjects recalled their family environment as significantly less cohesive than did the depressive subjects. For Time 2, borderline subjects' families were rated much lower on the cohesion subscale, as in Time 1, but much higher on the conflict subscale than were depressive families. Borderline patients also tended to rate their families lower on the organization subscale than did the depressive patients.

It was thought that borderline patients would score their families lower than would depressive patients on the personal growth dimension of the FES, which includes scales of independence, achievement orientation, intellectual-cultural orientation, and moral-religious emphasis. However, the t-tests indicated no significant difference between groups on any of these subscales. There was a nonsignificant trend for borderline patients to rate their families lower on both the moral-religious emphasis and the intellectual-cultural orientation subscales than did the depressive patients.

Finally, it was hypothesized that borderline patients, more so than depressive patients, would characterize their family environment as much more problematic during the adolescent period, when issues of separation-individuation become magnified for the family, than during childhood. Borderline patients were expected to have a higher score on conflict and lower scores on cohesion, expressiveness, independence, organization, or control in adolescence versus childhood. Within-group analysis using pairwise t tests was conducted to assess any differences between the two age periods, childhood (Time 1) and adolescence (Time 2). There were no significant group differences in ratings of their family environment between Time 1 and Time 2, except on one subscale. Borderline patients rated their family environment higher on the independence subscale (t(24) = 2.0981, P < .05) for Time 2, whereas depressive patients rated theirs lower on the control subscale (t(18) = 2.064, P < .05) for Time 2. The result for the borderline group is counterintuitive to the hypothesis that borderline subjects' family environments limit their independence during adolescence, although the mean score for Time 2 on the independence subscale was still relatively low (scaled score = 32).

Table 5-4. Mean scaled subscale scores on the Family Environment Scale (FES) between groups, Time 1 vs. Time 2

	BPD		MDD		
Subscale	Mean	SD	Mean	SD	t
Time 1 (ages 0–12)					
Cohesion	20	19	44	23	3.486*
Expressiveness	30	13	36	14	1.343
Conflict	61	15	54	15	1.503
Independence	26	16	31	18	.934
Achievement orientation	47	18	54	15	1.380
Intellectual-cultural orientation	34	13	42	16	1.845
Active-recreational orientation	38	12	43	14	1.461
Moral-religious emphasis	50	12	56	11	1.856
Organization	49	16	56	14	1.599
Control	59	14	65	8	1.715
Time 2 (ages 13–18)					
Cohesion	14	13	39	23	4.276**
Expressiveness	31	13	30	13	.238
Conflict	64	17	48	13	3.335*
Independence	33	17	38	23	.777
Achievement-orientation	53	18	55	15	.557
Intellectual-cultural orientation	36	13	42	15	1.427
Active-recreational orientation	42	12	46	16	.933
Moral-religious emphasis	47	11	53	14	1.375
Organization	47	14	56	16	1.894
Control	57	16	60	11	.722

Note. BPD = borderline personality disorder; MDD = major depressive disorder.
*P < .001. **P < .0001.

DISCUSSION

The results of this study have shown that certain childhood and adolescent experiences of borderline and depressed patients can be differentiated. The borderline group recalled having parents who were typically disabled by depression or substance abuse. Further, borderline patients experienced their parents as erratic and unstable in their functioning and interpersonal relationships. The descriptions of these parents indicated that they had substantial psychological limitations of which the subject was aware at a young age. Patients' descriptive recollections of parents in the family context often included how isolated the family was from the outside world, and how different they felt because of their parents. These data may imply psychological unavailability or neglect on the part of borderlines' parents, who seemed unable to meet adequately the emotional needs of their children (Gunderson and Englund 1981).

Interestingly, the frequency of separations and losses did not distinguish the two groups. Contrary to some of the current literature (Bradley 1979; Soloff and Millward 1983; Walsh 1977), borderline patients did not experience a significantly greater number of or more negative reactions to separation events than did depressive patients. Furthermore, and surprisingly, the typical family in both groups was intact and consisted of both biological parents. Loss events through death were not a common occurrence for either group. This result is consistent with Reich's study (1986), which found that the cluster of personality-disordered patients that included borderline patients reported significantly fewer deaths of parents compared with other psychiatric populations. Reich suggested that "to learn certain maladaptive coping patterns, both a father and a mother are required" (p. 172).

The greater frequency of sexual abuse in the borderline patients' histories as compared with those of depressive patients is a significant finding. We and others (Brooks 1982; Herman and van der Kolk 1987) have begun to explore more systematically this important finding and its possible relationship to borderline symptomatology. In a recent study, Herman et al. (1989) compared the abuse histories of borderline patients with a control group of psychiatric patients diagnosed with schizotypal or antisocial personality disorder, or bipolar II disorder. The borderline group reported, for the preadolescent years, a significantly higher incidence of physical abuse (71%), sexual abuse (68%), and witnessing domestic violence (62%) in comparison with the other psychiatric patients.

Previous studies have shown that women who reported abuses that were highly intrusive and of long duration and perpetrated by a father or stepfather experienced the most long-lasting negative effects (Herman et al. 1986). The subjects in our study encountered a variety of sexual abuse experiences ranging from one incident to many; fondling to penetration; and involving siblings, other relatives, and nonfamily individuals. They still reported long-lasting, problematic effects. It could be speculated that either the abuse was one of many factors that contributed to a highly pathological family system or that the abuse itself may be indicative of the extent of pathology within the family.

Consistent with the literature is the finding that adolescence is a critical period during the borderline subject's development. In this study, borderline patients experienced more conflict and less cohesion within the family during their adolescent years as compared with depressive patients. It could be speculated that the adolescent period spawned problems for the family at a time when identity and individuation issues became salient. Borderline adolescents experienced significant peer-related social problems in school, especially during the high-school years, further underscoring possible difficulty with identity and perhaps affectional relationships. Borderline subjects typically saw themselves as loners on the fringes of the junior-high and high-school social scene. Self descriptions such as "I didn't fit in," and "I felt lonely," "Nobody liked me," "I was an outcast," and "I didn't feel accepted" were typical responses. Although peer problems were evident as early as elementary school for many borderline subjects, they were usually not of the severity and quality of those during the high-school period.

Several authors have suggested that failure in social development for borderline individuals becomes most evident during this adolescent period. Grinker et al. (1968) remarked that borderline patients have developmental problems with two of Erikson's eight phases. They indicated that borderline patients experience "role confusion and lack of identity evidenced clearly in adolescence," and that they are "isolates and lack the capacity for intimacy or affiliation and love, revealed when the adult role should have been attained" (p. 146). Grinker et al. further found that the defenses of withdrawal and intellectualization were most typically used by the borderline patient. Loneliness was defended against with alcohol, drugs, and sexual promiscuity. Goldstein and Jones (1977) speculated that a pattern of severe isolation and withdrawal during adolescence contributed to borderline development. Similarly, Vaillant (1987) believed that "personality disorder reflects issues and failures in adolescent development just as much as it does issues in child development" (p. 148).

To summarize, we can speculate that borderline patients recall their family experiences as a combination of traumatic early events, psychologically unavailable parents, and family conflict, all reflecting a nonnurturing, unstable environment. A pattern of emotional neglect probably characterized the borderline patients' experiences with parents. Mothers typically had psychiatric disorders in the form of depression and/or a personality disorder; fathers were likely to abuse alcohol. This was complicated by the traumatic experiences of sexual abuse at the hands of not only family members but nonfamily individuals. The impact of these early developmental experiences begins to show its negative effects in elementary school and becomes magnified during the adolescent years. Interpersonal problems rooted in early parental deprivation and the lack of appropriate role models may have contributed to difficulties in establishing age-appropriate relationships in school. The borderline individual fails to develop the ego identity and relatedness necessary to integrate successfully with peers and consequently views himself or herself as a loner, isolated and separate from others. He or she may then turn to drugs and promiscuity as avenues of interpersonal contact.

LIMITATIONS OF THE STUDY AND FUTURE DIRECTIONS

Some issues of methodology tend to limit or confound the findings. First, we measured borderline patients' recollections of childhood events. Any study that depends on memory is certainly going to be tainted by distortions, with even greater distortions among borderline patients, who tend to split, project, idealize, devalue, and externalize (Gunderson 1984; Kernberg 1975). Further, all of our subjects were inpatients, and the stressors that led to the subjects' hospitalization may have further added to the degree of distortion in reporting past events.

In addition, many of our subjects were suffering from a mood disorder that also might further increase the distortion in their recollections. We attempted to reduce the effect of mood by giving each subject a specific series of life events to which he or she had to respond. However, this method cannot compare with a prospective study design in which high-risk or targeted populations are identified early in life and followed through to adulthood.

Our subjects were predominantly female, consistent with the notion that BPD is found predominantly in females. They matched well with the depressed group on this variable, but their almost exclusive inclusion in the study does not allow for more complete generalizability of the findings. Although it has been theorized that the BPD might be viewed primarily as a disorder of impulse (Loranger and Tulis 1985), males and females may certainly express these impulses in different ways. Perhaps comparing family history data of borderline patients with those of antisocial personality disorder patients, cohorts that Perry (1988) is currently studying, may help uncover familial patterns, experiences, and events common to both disorders.

Future studies in this area should incorporate samples taken from various clinical settings, for it is difficult to generalize findings obtained from inpatients in a university hospital setting to outpatients in long-term psychotherapy. Finally, it would be useful to evaluate directly as many family members as possible. In this way, independent evaluations of each family member's interpersonal functioning and psychiatric conditions could be more accurately assessed, and historical information given by the patient could be confirmed or refuted. This might then provide us with a clearer conceptualization of the life events, stressors, and traumata that are significant in the development of borderline psychopathology.

REFERENCES

Akiskal HS, Chen SE, Davis GC, et al: Borderline: an adjective in search of a noun. J Clin Psychiatry 46:41–48, 1985

American Psychiatric Association: Diagnostic and Statistical Manual of Mental Disorders, 3rd Edition. Washington, DC, American Psychiatric Association, 1980

Bradley SJ: The relationship of early maternal separation to borderline personality in children and adolescents: a pilot study. Am J Psychiatry 136:424–426, 1979

Brooks B: Familial influences in father-daughter incest. Journal of Psychiatric Treatment and Evaluation 4:117–124, 1982

Charney DS, Nelson JC, Quinlan DM: Personality traits and disorder in depression. Am J Psychiatry 138:1601–1604, 1981

Cohen J: Weighted kappa: nominal scale agreement with provision for scaled disagreement of partial credit. Psychol Bull 70:213–220, 1968

Cornell DG, Silk KR, Ludolph PS, et al: Test-retest reliability of the diagnostic interview for borderlines. Arch Gen Psychiatry 40:1307–1310, 1981

Gaviria M, Flaherty J, Val E: A comparison of bipolar patients with and without a borderline personality disorder. Psychiatr J Univ Ottawa 7:190–195, 1982

Goldstein MJ, Jones JE: Adolescent and familial precursors of borderline and schizophrenic conditions, in Borderline Personality Disorder. Edited by

Hartocollis P. New York, International Universities Press, 1977, pp 213–229

Greenman DA, Gunderson JG, Cane M, et al: An examination of the borderline diagnosis in children. Am J Psychiatry 143:998–1003, 1986

Grinker RR, Werble B, Drye RC: The Borderline Syndrome: A Behavioral Study of Ego-Functions. New York, Basic Books, 1968

Gunderson JG: Borderline Personality Disorder. Washington, DC, American Psychiatric Press, 1984

Gunderson JG, Elliot GR: The interface between borderline personality disorder and affective disorder. Am J Psychiatry 142:277–288, 1985

Gunderson JG, Englund DW: Characterizing the families of borderlines: a review of the literature. Psychiatr Clin North Am 4:159–168, 1981

Gunderson JG, Singer MP: Defining borderline patients: an overview. Am J Psychiatry 132:1–10, 1975

Gunderson JG, Kolb JE, Austin Y: The diagnostic interview for borderline patients. Am J Psychiatry 138:896–903, 1981

Herman J, van der Kolk BA: Traumatic antecedents of borderline personality disorder, in Psychological Trauma. Edited by van der Kolk BA. Washington, DC, American Psychiatric Press, 1987, pp 111–126

Herman J, Russell D, Trocki K: Long-term effects of incestuous abuse in childhood. Am J Psychiatry 143:1293–1296, 1986

Herman JL, Perry JC, van der Kolk BA: Childhood trauma in borderline personality disorder. Am J Psychiatry 146:490–495, 1989

Kernberg O: Borderline Conditions and Pathological Narcissism. New York, Jason Aronson, 1975

Kroll J, Ogata S: The relationship of borderline personality disorder to the affective disorders. Psychiatr Dev 2:105–128, 1987

Loranger AW, Tulis EH: Family history of alcoholism in borderline personality disorder. Arch Gen Psychiatry 42:153–157, 1985

Mahler M, Pine F, Bergman A: The Psychological Birth of the Human Infant: Symbiosis and Individuation. New York, Basic Books, 1975

Masterson J: Treatment of the Borderline Adolescent: A Developmental Approach. New York, John Wiley, 1972

Masterson J: The Psychotherapy of the Borderline Adult. New York, Brunner/Mazel, 1976

Moos R, Moos B: Family Environment Scale Manual. Palo Alto, CA, Consulting Psychological Press, 1981

Ogata SN, Silk KR, Goodrich S, et al: Childhood abuse and clinical symptoms in borderline patients. Paper presented at the annual meeting of the American Psychiatric Association, Montreal, May 1988

Perry JC: A prospective study of life stress, defenses, psychotic symptoms, and depression in borderline and antisocial personality disorder and bipolar type II affective disorder. Journal of Personality Disorders 2:49–59, 1988

Reich J: The relationship between early life events and DSM-III personality disorders. Hillside J Clin Psychiatry 8:164–173, 1986

Soloff PH, Millward JW: Developmental histories of borderline patients. Compr Psychiatry 24:574–588, 1983

Spitzer RL, Endicott JE, Robins E: Research diagnostic criteria—rationale and reliability. Arch Gen Psychiatry 35:773–782, 1978

Stone MH: Borderline syndromes: a consideration of subtypes, and an overview; directions for research. Psychiatr Clin North Am 4:3–23, 1981

Vaillant GE: A developmental view of old and new perspectives of personality disorders. Journal of Personality Disorders 1:146–156, 1987

Walsh F: Family studies 1976: fourteen new borderline cases, in The Borderline Patient. Edited by Grinker RR, Werble B. New York, Jason Aronson, 1977, pp 158–177

Chapter 6

Sexual Abuse and Biparental Failure as Etiologic Models in Borderline Personality Disorder

Paul S. Links, M.D., M.Sc., F.R.C.P.(C)
Ingrid Boiago, B.A., R.N.
Gail Huxley, R.N.
Meir Steiner, M.D., Ph.D.
Janice E. Mitton, R.N., B.A., M.H.Sc.

Chapter 6

Sexual Abuse and Biparental Failure as Etiologic Models in Borderline Personality Disorder

Possible etiologic models for the development of borderline personality disorder (BPD) were proposed in Chapter 1. The purpose of this chapter is to test empirically two of the etiologic models: the impact of sexual abuse in childhood and the effects of biparental failure. Our discussion will begin by outlining specific issues related to each of these hypotheses that will lend themselves to empirical examination. Following the presentation of the methods and findings, the discussion will suggest research approaches that may be used to test further these etiologic models.

Herman was one of the first authors to draw clear attention to the possible etiologic significance of traumata during childhood as causing BPD (Herman and van der Kolk 1987). Herman and van der Kolk criticized earlier psychodynamic writers who discounted the idea of abuse and believed these reports to be part of the patient's self-serving distortions of reality. These authors raised two important issues. First, they drew an analogy between the descriptions of chronic post-traumatic stress disorder (PTSD) and BPD. In both syndromes, major disturbances are found in affect regulation, impulse control, reality testing, interpersonal relationships, and self-integration. Using this analogy, the authors suggested that the occurrence of significant childhood traumata may be the etiologic mechanism producing BPD. Second, they proposed that incest and sexual abuse may be of particular significance in explaining the development of BPD. Sexual abuse is known to be perpetrated much more commonly against girls than boys; therefore, the occurrence of sexual abuse may explain the female predominance found in BPD. Stone (1981) suggested that incestuous experiences may be a major etiologic factor producing this disorder in females. Sexual abuse is more likely to be perpetrated over a prolonged period of time, and therefore, fits with the model that chronic stress rather than a single traumatic episode leads to significant adult maladjustment that mimics chronic PTSD.

Herman et al. (1988) tested their etiologic hypotheses by examining the backgrounds of 21 subjects with DSM-III (American Psychiatric Association 1980) BPD: 11 subjects with borderline traits and 23 subjects with the near-neighbor diagnoses of schizotypal or antisocial personality disorder or bipolar II affective disorder. The great majority of borderline patients had experienced childhood traumata: 71% had been physically abused, 68% had been sexually abused, and 62% had witnessed domestic violence. The history of early childhood abuse or traumata was found almost exclusively in borderline subjects: 57% of BPD subjects, 9% of subjects with borderline traits, and 13% of subjects with near-neighbor diagnoses experienced traumata before the age of 6. In addition, the BPD subjects suffered significantly more types of trauma, beginning at an earlier age, and repeated over a longer period of time. Therefore, Herman et al. (1989), like others, substantiated the frequent occurrence of traumatic antecedents in the childhood histories of BPD patients, and they found that the traumata were chronically experienced beginning in early childhood.

This study also examined whether the experience of childhood traumata was related to the occurrence of dissociative phenomena. Similar connections have been made between dissociation and PTSD (Spiegel et al. 1988). Herman et al. (1989) did not find dissociative experiences to be characteristic of BPD subjects, but high levels of dissociative symptoms were reported by all subjects with personality disorders.

Herman's work suggests that childhood sexual abuse may be a distinct pathway leading to BPD and that it is unrelated to other proposed etiologic models such as the occurrence of separation and loss during childhood. Also, patients who were sexually abused present with clinical features that closely mimic those of chronic PTSD.

The interest in parental failure of both parents of borderline patients comes from both clinical observation and empirical work. Feldman and Guttman (1984) observed that borderline patients may be more vulnerable because they lack a positive/protective relationship with the nonabusive parent. They had observed this mechanism in their clinical work with the families of borderline children, adolescents, and adults, or with couples in whom one spouse was borderline. They noted interactional patterns in which the parent without significant psychopathology failed to protect the child from the parent with psychopathology.

In Chapter 1, some of the empirical work that suggested the frequent occurrence of biparental failure in the families of borderline patients was reviewed (Akiskal et al. 1985; Frank and Paris 1981; Gunderson et al. 1980; Soloff and Millward 1983). Akiskal et al. (1985) proposed that the offspring from families in which both parents had psychiatric illness may be at a double disadvantage: they may inherit the illnesses of one or both parents, and they may develop an exquisite vulnerability to adult object loss as a result of the tempestuous early home environment.

To examine the impact of sexual abuse in childhood, two hypotheses are addressed. First, the reporting given by inpatients with BPD of sexual abuse perpetrated by primary caregivers is hypothesized to be unrelated to the occurrence of separation or loss experiences in childhood. Second, inpatients with BPD who have experienced sexual abuse perpetrated by their primary caregivers are hypothesized to evidence a majority of the characteristics of PTSD more frequently than nonsexually abused patients (Herman and van der Kolk 1987).

To examine the etiologic model of biparental failure, we studied those families in which both parents received psychiatric diagnoses. According to this model, the probands from these families are at an increased risk for traumatic and separation or loss experiences during childhood. As a result of suffering a double disadvantage, the probands from these families may have a more chronic, severe borderline disorder, and their siblings may be at increased risk for BPD.

Our own study of a cohort of borderline inpatients provided an opportunity to test these etiologic models further (Links et al. 1988b). Antecedent information had been collected, and we found that inpatients meeting the Diagnostic Interview for Borderlines (DIB) (Gunderson et al. 1981) criteria for BPD were significantly more likely than patients with borderline traits to report having been separated from their mother for more than 3 months, been placed in a foster home, and come from a home with a nonintact marriage in childhood. The BPD inpatients more frequently reported being physically (29.4% vs. 9.1%, $P \le .007$) and sexually (25.9% vs. 11.8%, $P \le .02$) abused by their primary caregivers than patients with borderline traits (Links et al. 1988b). In addition, all first-degree relatives of the BPD patients had been examined for borderline and other psychiatric diagnoses (Links et al. 1988a). Our findings suggest that the morbid risk for BPD was increased in the first-degree relatives of the borderline probands.

METHODS

Patients of either sex and between the ages of 18 and 65 years admitted between July 1, 1983, and December 31, 1985, to acute psychiatric inpatient facilities associated with McMaster University, Faculty of Health Sciences, Department of Psychiatry, Hamilton, Ontario, were eligible for inclusion into the study.

Admitted patients were consecutively screened for borderline characteristics, using the discriminative features of Gunderson and Kolb (1978). These clinical features (low achievement, impulsivity, manipulative suicide, heightened affectivity, mild psychotic experiences, high socialization, and disturbed close relationships) were found to be the best overall discriminators between borderline patients and those with other disorders. Patients with three or more of the seven features were then seen by an experienced research nurse. Patients were excluded at this point if they evidenced

- A primary diagnosis of alcoholism or drug habituation as the primary reason for the current admission
- Organicity based on clinical evidence of central nervous system abnormality of any etiology
- Any physical disorders of known psychiatric significance
- Borderline mental retardation as confirmed by a verbal IQ score of less than 80 using the Peabody Picture Vocabulary Test (Dunn and Dunn 1981)
- A history of hospitalization for more than 2 years cumulatively of the previous 5
- Inability to understand English

Patients meeting our inclusion criteria were asked for written informed consent. With their consent, the patients were then interviewed using the Schedule for Affective Disorders and Schizophrenia (SADS) Current and Lifetime versions (Endicott and Spitzer 1978), and the DIB. Results from the SADS were applied to Research Diagnostic Criteria (RDC) (Spitzer et al. 1981) to obtain diagnoses for both the current and lifetime episodes of psychiatric illness. The SADS and the DIB were combined in a manner similar to that used by Loranger et al. (1984), who demonstrated the reliability of supplementing the SADS to obtain the DIB. The patients were asked about their childhood upbringing. Questions related to separations from mother for more than 3 months were derived from Bradley (1979), and questions on foster home placement and physical and sexual abuse perpetrated by the primary caregivers were taken from Reitsma-Street et al. (1985). Evidence of school failure and antisocial behavior during childhood was elicited.

All consenting first-degree family members over 18 years of age of our probands who lived within a radius of 100 kilometers around the greater metropolitan Hamilton, Ontario, area were interviewed directly. The interview included completion of the SADS, Lifetime version, to which RDC were applied. To diagnose BPD in family members, those who were directly interviewed were given the DIB and were considered borderline if they scored 7 or more.

For family members who were unavailable, were deceased, or refused to participate, or when the proband refused consent to have family members contacted, either a respondent was chosen from the available family members or the proband served as the informant. This person provided information on the relatives, and diagnoses were made using Family History Research Diagnostic Criteria (Andreasen et al. 1977). The diagnosis of BPD is not included in this method; therefore, there was a need to devise a procedure for diagnosing BPD from the indirect interview. As false negatives are a greater problem using indirect family data, less stringent criteria for the diagnosis were chosen (Andreasen et al. 1977). To receive the diagnosis of BPD based on the indirect interview, the family member had to have demonstrated, at some time in his or her adult life, three of the seven discriminating features as described by Gunderson and Kolb (1978), and these features had to occur concurrently.

Family data were collected on 69 of the 88 (78.4%) probands. Eleven of the probands refused to have their families involved and were unwilling to act as the informant. Eight of the 88 probands (9.1%) had been adopted, so data on their biological family members were unavailable. Information was obtained on 320 family members; 114 (36%) were interviewed directly, and 206 (64%) were diagnosed based on indirect data. Diagnostic information on both biological parents was available from 61 families. Information was not available for four fathers and five mothers.

RESULTS

Sexual Abuse

Table 6-1 demonstrates the correlations between the antecedent variables studied as possible etiologic factors in BPD. Sexual abuse perpetrated by primary caregivers was significantly related to physical abuse at the hands of the primary caregivers (phi statistic = 0.24, $n =$ 84, $P < .05$) but was not significantly related to separations from mother for 3 months during childhood, foster home placement, or the occurrence of nonintact parental marriage. As shown in Table 6-1, the other factors were significantly intercorrelated. BPD inpatients with a history of sexual abuse were compared to those with no history of sexual abuse on the 29 scored statements taken from the DIB, and on diagnostic items taken from the DSM-III schizotypal and borderline personality disorder criteria. As shown in Tables 6-2 and 6-3, the abused borderline patients evidenced more self-mutilation, substance abuse, recurrent illusions, depersonalization, derealization, and physically self-damaging acts. Although uncommon, manic episodes, persistent delusions, or hallucinations were more often reported by the abused than the nonabused borderline patients. The other items taken from the DIB and the DSM-III criteria did not differentiate the abused from nonabused subgroups. The abused BPD probands scored significantly higher on the impulse action pattern subscale score of the DIB (6.91 vs. 5.33; $t = 3.05$, $df = 83$, $P = .003$) and on the total section score of the DIB (29.9 vs. 27.4; $t = 1.99$, $df = 83$, $P = .05$). The abused subgroup scored significantly lower on the Peabody Picture Vocabulary Test screening IQ test (91.0 vs. 99.8; $t = 2.32$, $P = .023$) and showed a trend toward poorer school records than the nonabused subgroup. The abused and nonabused subgroups were not significantly differentiated by sex distribution or occupational status.

Biparental Failure

The distribution of diagnoses among the biological parents of the

Table 6-1. Correlation between proposed etiologic factors

Etiologic factor	SA	PA	S	FP	PM
Sexual abuse (SA)		.24^{+}*	.07	.16	.03
		(84)	(81)	(83)	(84)
Physical abuse (PA)			.26*	.23*	.30**
			(82)	(84)	(84)
Separations (S)				.45***	.31**
				(83)	(82)
Foster home placement (FP)					.22*
					(84)
Nonintact parental marriage (PM)					

Note. $^{+}$ denotes (phi correlation)/N.
*$P < .05$. **$P < .01$. ***$P < .001$.

Table 6-2. Diagnostic items differentiating sexually abused from nonabused probands

Diagnostic Interview for Borderlines items[a]	Abused n (%)	Nonabused n (%)	Significance
Self-mutilation	17/22 (77.3)	30/63 (47.6)	$P = .02$
Substance abuse	16/22 (72.7)	21/63 (33.3)	$P = .005$
Manic episodes/ persistent delusions/ hallucinations	4/22 (18.2)	1/63 (1.6)	$P = .015$

[a]All other items did not significantly differentiate subgroups.

Table 6-3. Comparison of sexually abused and nonabused probands on DSM-III items

DSM-III Items	Abused n (%)	Nonabused n (%)	Significance
Schizotypal items			
Magical thinking	3/22 (13.6)	2/61 (3.3)	NS
Ideas of reference	0/22	1/60 (1.7)	NS
Social isolation	3/22 (13.6)	7/61 (11.5)	NS
Recurrent illusions, depersonalization, derealization	8/22 (36.4)	4/60 (6.7)	$P = .001$
Odd speech	0/22	0/60	
Inadequate rapport	0/22	2/60 (3.3)	NS
Suspicious/paranoid ideation	8/22 (36.4)	14/60 (23.3)	NS
Undue social anxiety	1/22 (4.5)	2/60 (3.3)	NS
Borderline items			
Impulsivity	20/22 (90.9)	50/59 (84.7)	NS
Unstable/intense relationship	17/19 (89.5)	41/59 (69.5)	NS
Inappropriate intense anger	15/21 (71.4)	42/58 (72.4)	NS
Identity disturbance	8/21 (38.1)	29/57 (50.9)	NS
Affective instability	13/21 (61.9)	28/59 (47.5)	NS
Intolerance of being alone	15/20 (75.0)	35/55 (63.6)	NS
Physically self-damaging acts	20/21 (95.2)	41/59 (69.5)	$P = .017$
Emptiness, boredom	16/20 (80.0)	55/60 (91.7)	NS

BPD probands indicated that 21 of 61 (34.4%) families had parents without psychiatric diagnoses, 23 of 61 (37.7%) families had one parent with a psychiatric diagnosis, and 17 of 61 (27.9%) families had both parents diagnosed as having a psychiatric disorder.

Table 6-4 lists the diagnoses based on RDC for the parents, where both parents were diagnosed. The majority received multiple diagnoses (18 of 34; 52.9%), and no particular pairing of diagnoses between spouses was evident.

The three subgroups of probands based on parental history of psychiatric illness showed a significantly different sex distribution. The subgroup with parents with no diagnosis included 23.8% (5 of 21) males versus 0% (0 of 23) and 11.8% (2 of 17) males in the families with one parent diagnosed and both parents diagnosed, respectively.

The probands from the subgroup with both parents diagnosed had significantly poorer school records than each of the other two subgroups. They also left school at a significantly younger age than the subgroup with one parent diagnosed (16.3 vs. 18.4 years, respectively).

The occurrence of the other proposed etiologic factors across the three subgroups by parental diagnosis is shown in Table 6-5. All the purported causal factors were significantly more frequently found in the childhood histories of probands who came from families in which both parents received psychiatric diagnoses.

DIB Total Section Score, age of first outpatient care, number of psychiatric hospitalizations, age of first hospitalization, and total time of psychiatric hospitalizations did not differentiate the subgroups from one another. As shown in Table 6-6, the families with both parents diagnosed had a significantly higher prevalence of siblings who also received the diagnosis of BPD.

DISCUSSION

We examined whether childhood sexual abuse may be a distinct etiologic pathway leading to BPD. This hypothesis was somewhat supported by the fact that reporting of sexual abuse was not significantly related to occurrence of separation or loss experiences in childhood. Using the analogy of PTSD, Herman and van der Kolk (1987) suggested that sexual abuse in childhood, which is likely to be persistent, may lead to a constellation of symptoms in borderline patients that are part of the PTSD. Most of the items taken from DIB and DSM-III criteria that covered the concepts of interest were not significantly more likely to be reported by sexually abused versus nonsexually abused probands. However, the sexually abused borderline patients were characterized by having more evidence of self-

Table 6-4. Diagnoses by Research Diagnostic Criteria in patients where both parents were diagnosed

Patient No.	Mother	Father
1	Depression[a]	Depression
2	Depression, recurrent depression	Depression, recurrent depression, other diagnosis[b]
3	Depression, recurrent depression	Depression, ASPD, other diagnosis, BPD
4	Depression, alcoholism, drug abuse, unspecified psychosis, other diagnosis, recurrent depression	Alcoholism
5	Depression, recurrent depression	Depression, bipolar affective disorder, alcoholism, ASPD, unspecified psychosis, other diagnosis, BPD
6	Schizoaffective-depressed	Alcoholism
7	Depression, recurrent depression	Alcoholism
8	Alcoholism	Depression, other diagnosis
9	Depression, recurrent depression, alcoholism	Depression, recurrent depression, alcoholism, ASPD, BPD, other diagnosis
10	Depression	Alcoholism, ASPD, BPD
11	Alcoholism	Alcoholism, BPD
12	Depression, recurrent depression, other diagnosis	Depression, alcoholism, other diagnosis
13	Schizoaffective-depressed, mania, alcoholism, drug abuse, recurrent depression, BPD	Depression
14	Depression, recurrent depression, drug abuse	Alcoholism
15	Depression, alcoholism, drug abuse, recurrent depression, other diagnosis, BPD	Alcoholism
16	Alcoholism	Alcoholism, ASPD
17	Depression	Other diagnosis

Note. ASPD = antisocial personality disorder; BPD = borderline personality disorder.
[a]Current episode at time of interview. [b] Evidence of significant psychopathology not clearly classifiable.

Table 6-5. Relationship of parent's diagnoses to other proposed etiologic factors

Family grouping by parental diagnosis	Separations n (%)	Foster home placement n (%)	Nonintact marriage n (%)	Sexual abuse n (%)	Physical abuse n (%)
No parental diagnosis	1/21 (4.8)	1/21 (4.8)	3/21 (14.3)	4/21 (19.0)	1/21 (4.8)
Father/mother only	6/22 (27.3)	2/22 (9.1)	7/23 (30.4)	3/23 (13.0)	5/23 (21.7)
Both parents	8/16 (50.0)**	7/17 (41.2)**	11/17 (64.7)***	7/15 (46.7)*	7/16 (43.8)*

*P < .05. **P < .01. ***P < .005.

mutilation, substance abuse, other physically self-damaging acts, recurrent illusions, depersonalization, and derealization. These features have been reported to be found in adults as a result of the long-term effects of sexual abuse in childhood (Ogata et al. 1988). The characteristics of PTSD were not confined to those borderline patients who had been sexually abused by their primary caregivers. Other childhood traumata appear to be capable of producing these features. However, our data suggest that these sexually abused borderline patients will be much more likely to carry out self-damaging acts, report dissociative experiences, and abuse drugs.

These findings may have importance for further clarifying the etiologic models in two ways. First, if childhood sexual abuse is the factor leading to adult impulsivity, drug abuse, and dissociative experiences, then interventions targeted at resolving the issues of the abuse experience might be expected to affect these symptoms specifically. Group therapy has been proposed as helpful in resolving the experience of childhood sexual abuse (van der Kolk 1987). A randomized control trial of this approach versus less targeted therapy with sexually abused borderline patients will hypothetically have the greatest effect on impulsivity, drug abuse, and dissociative experiences. Designing a treatment study that addresses an etiologic hypothesis has the potential to unravel the issues of etiology while assisting patient management. Other research designs that could be used to test this etiologic model appear to be unwieldy. For example, a prospective cohort study of children exposed to sexual abuse versus those not exposed would require years of follow-up and careful delineation of confounding variables.

Childhood sexual abuse, although it may not be a specific causative factor, may be important as a marker that can delineate a specific subgroup of borderline patients. Our data suggest that the patients in this subgroup may be at greater risk for suffering the consequences of their impulsivity and drug abuse and, thus, may have a poorer prognosis than nonsexually abused borderline patients.

Table 6-6. Prevalence of siblings with borderline personality disorder

Family grouping by parental diagnosis	Siblings *n* (%)
No parental diagnosis	3/59 (5.1)
Father/mother only	10/69 (14.5)
Both parents diagnosed	16/43 (37.2)[a]

[a]$\chi^2 = 18.10$, $df = 2$, $P = .0001$.

Biparental failure, as evidenced by both parents in a family receiving a psychiatric diagnosis, was found in 28% of our sample. The significant relationship between the prevalence of BPD in the proband's siblings and the occurrence of biparental failure was suggestive of this characteristic being an etiologic factor in BPD. Not all cases of BPD were attributable to this factor, and biparental failure was not related to the chronicity or severity of BPD. Biparental failure was significantly related to the other proposed etiologic factors, and, intuitively, this may suggest that parental psychiatric illness may be responsible for producing these other proposed risk factors.

If biparental failure is an important etiologic factor, then future attention should be directed at understanding what the proximal mechanisms are that lead the child to be maladjusted. By clarifying the proximal mechanisms or the causal chain of events leading to a disorder, the possibilities for developing preventive strategies are greatly enhanced (Rutter 1982). With the present data, we can explore further possible mechanisms that can lead to new, more detailed etiologic models. For example, Rutter and Quinton (1984) suggested that parental psychopathology and offspring maladjustment may be due to the parent's symptoms having direct impact on the child's learning or development. Our data might support this notion, as probands with two disordered parents had worse school records and left school earlier than those children in the comparison subgroups.

Rutter and Quinton (1984) also hypothesized that parental psychopathology may act through marital dysfunction. As a partial test of this hypothesis, we selected those families with both parents having psychiatric diagnoses and compared those with intact versus nonintact marriages for the prevalence of BPD in the siblings. In families with intact marriages, 7 of 14 (50%) siblings were diagnosed BPD versus 9 of 29 (31%) siblings from nonintact marriages. Therefore, the occurrence of nonintact marriages did not interact with biparental failure to produce increased prevalence of BPD. From our data, one might elaborate a theory that suggests that the child's learning and development are particularly vulnerable to having two parents with psychiatric illness.

The present study must be considered as a preliminary examination of the proposed etiological models for several reasons. First, our case control design cannot determine the direction of cause and effect. Children with an inherent tendency toward impulsive behavior may be more likely to be victims of abuse rather than their impulsivity being the outcome of exposure to abuse. Second, the definition of causative agents used in this study may have been unduly conservative.

For example, the occurrence of sexual abuse was limited to those episodes perpetrated by the primary caregivers; therefore, many of the borderline inpatients in the comparison group may have been sexually abused by other individuals. The definition of biparental failure was limited to families in which both parents received psychiatric diagnoses; however, parents may fail to carry out parental functions for many other reasons. Finally, some significant findings may be expected by chance using the 29 items from the DIB because of the multiple analyses. Despite these cautions, the proposed etiologic models of childhood sexual abuse and biparental failure do hold promise and deserve further study.

REFERENCES

Akiskal HS, Chen ES, Davis GC, et al: Borderline: an adjective in search of a noun. J Clin Psychiatry 46:41–48, 1985

American Psychiatric Association: Diagnostic and Statistical Manual of Mental Disorders, 3rd Edition. Washington, DC, American Psychiatric Association, 1980

Andreasen NC, Endicott J, Spitzer RL, et al: The family history method using diagnostic criteria: reliability and validity. Arch Gen Psychiatry 34:1229–1235, 1977

Bradley SJ: The relationship of early maternal separation to borderline personality in children and adolescents: a pilot study. Am J Psychiatry 136:424–426, 1979

Dunn LM, Dunn LM: Peabody Picture Vocabulary Test—Revised. Circle Pines, MN, American Guidance Service, 1981

Endicott J, Spitzer RL: A diagnostic interview: the Schedule for Affective Disorders and Schizophrenia. Arch Gen Psychiatry 35:837–844, 1978

Feldman RB, Guttman HA: Families of borderline patients: literal-minded parents, borderline parents and parental protectiveness. Am J Psychiatry 141:1392–1396, 1984

Frank H, Paris J: Recollections of family experience in borderline patients. Arch Gen Psychiatry 38:1031–1034, 1981

Gunderson JG, Kolb JE: Discriminating features of borderline patients. Am J Psychiatry 135:792–796, 1978

Gunderson JG, Kerr J, Englund DW: The families of borderlines: a comparative study. Arch Gen Psychiatry 37:27–33, 1980

Gunderson JG, Kolb JE, Austin V: The diagnostic interview for borderline patients. Am J Psychiatry 138:896–903, 1981

Herman JL, van der Kolk B: Traumatic antecedents of borderline personality disorder, in Psychological Trauma. Edited by van der Kolk B. Washington, DC, American Psychiatric Press, 1987, pp 111–126

Herman JL, Perry JC, van der Kolk BA: Childhood trauma in borderline personality disorder. Am J Psychiatry 146:490–495, 1989

Links PS, Steiner M, Huxley G: The occurrence of borderline personality disorder in the families of borderline patients. Journal of Personality Disorders 2:14–20, 1988a

Links PS, Steiner M, Offord DR, et al: Characteristics of borderline personality disorder: a Canadian study. Can J Psychiatry 33:336–340, 1988b

Loranger AW, Oldham JM, Russakoff IM, et al: Structured interviews and borderline personality disorder. Arch Gen Psychiatry 41:565–568, 1984

Ogata SN, Silk KR, Goodrich S, et al: Childhood abuse and clinical symptoms in borderline patients. Paper presented at the annual meeting of the American Psychiatric Association, Montreal, Quebec, May 1988

Reitsma-Street M, Offord DR, Finch T: Pairs of same-sexed siblings discordant for antisocial behaviour. Br J Psychiatry 146:415–423, 1985

Rutter M: Prevention of children's psychosocial disorders: myth and substance. Pediatrics 70:883–894, 1982

Rutter M, Quinton D: Parental psychiatric disorder: effects on children. Psychol Med 14:853–880, 1984

Soloff PH, Millward JW: Developmental histories of borderline patients. Compr Psychiatry 24:547–588, 1983

Spiegel D, Hunt T, Dondershire HC: Dissociation and hypnotizability in post traumatic stress disorder. Am J Psychiatry 145:301–305, 1988

Spitzer RL, Endicott J, Robins E: Research Diagnostic Criteria (RDC) for a Selected Group of Functional Disorders, 3rd Edition. New York, New York State Psychiatric Institute, 1981

Stone MH: Borderline syndrome: a consideration of subtypes and an overview, directions for research. Psychiatr Clin North Am 4:3–24, 1981

van der Kolk BA: The role of the group in the origin and resolution of the trauma response, in Psychological Trauma. Edited by van der Kolk B. Washington, DC, American Psychiatric Press, 1987, pp 153–171

Chapter 7

Empirical Investigation of the Role of Development in the Etiology and Outcome of Borderline Personality Disorder

Joel Paris, M.D.

Chapter 7

Empirical Investigation of the Role of Development in the Etiology and Outcome of Borderline Personality Disorder

The purpose of this review is to examine the effects of developmental variables on the etiology and outcome of borderline personality disorder (BPD). There is evidence from a variety of empirically based reports that BPD patients have had an abnormal childhood. The particular nature of the abnormality is a matter of dispute. Factors that have been suggested to contribute to borderline pathology are neglect, abuse, and overprotection.

ETIOLOGY

Evidence for Neglect

Early uncontrolled observations on borderline patients by Grinker (1968) and Walsh (1968) suggested that the family experience of borderline patients is characterized by neglect and negativity. Bradley (1979) and Soloff and Millward (1983) described a high incidence of separation and loss of parents in early childhood in borderline patients. Using observations from family interviews conducted at the time of admission, Gunderson et al. (1980) found a pattern of biparental neglect, with the borderline patient scapegoated and isolated by parental coalition. Such observations could represent a reaction to pathology rather than a cause, but the recollected histories of borderline patients also suggest familial dysfunction and biparental neglect. Three studies (Frank and Hoffman, 1987; Frank and Paris, 1981; Paris and Frank, in press) using data bases of recollections of childhood showed that borderline patients remember not being cared for by either of their parents. Feldman and Guttman (1984) suggest that some borderline patients experience an emotional unresponsiveness from both parents akin to alexithymia.

Evidence for Abuse

Stone (1987), Ogata et al. (1988), Herman et al. (1989), and Zanarini et al. (1989) all found a high frequency of physical or sexual abuse in borderline patient histories. The presence of abuse histories in BPD patients is the basis for a major hypothesis to explain borderline pathology as a posttraumatic disorder. It is not clear to what extent sexual abuse interacts with parental neglect, or whether histories of sexual abuse are primarily intrafamilial rather than extrafamilial.

Evidence for Overprotection

Masterson (1981) theorized that borderline patients are unable to individuate from mothers, and that they may have mothers who are themselves borderline. Soloff and Millward (1983) have reported a pattern of overinvolved mothers and underinvolved fathers in a borderline sample; however, only the father findings were significantly different from comparison groups of depressive patients and schizophrenic patients. Moreover, none of the studies discussed above under neglect and abuse are consistent with the Masterson hypothesis. One possibility is that Masterson's patients were not strictly borderline by DSM-III-R (American Psychiatric Association 1987) or Gunderson and Singer (1975) criteria. It is also possible, as suggested by Feldman and Guttman (1984), that there are several routes to becoming borderline, one of which involves having a borderline mother. However, studies of the familial prevalence of borderline personality by Links et al. (1988) indicate that, although first-degree relatives are more often borderline, most mothers of borderline patients are not themselves borderline.

In summary, there is reasonably strong evidence from a number of different sources that borderline patients suffer from developmental trauma, and that these trauma are more severe than seen in comparison groups of patients with less disabling pathology.

OUTCOME

Recently, four studies of 15-year outcome of borderline patients have been published (McGlashan 1986; Paris et al. 1987; Plakun et al. 1986; Stone et al. 1987). They all showed long-term improvement for most patients, with mean levels of impairment in global functioning in the mild range, and loss of active symptomatology. However, suicide rates between 8.5% (Paris et al. 1987) and 9.5% (Stone et al.

1987) were found by two of the three studies that examined suicide. A lower rate in the third study (McGlashan 1986) was most likely due to a preselection of cases entering chronic hospitalization. These findings raise the question of how predictable global outcome or suicide is in these patients. Clinical variables such as IQ and affective instability predict global outcome (McGlashan 1985), whereas suicide is associated with higher education and previous attempts (Paris et al. 1989). Plakun (1988) found that long-term outcome was significantly worse in patients with a history of parental divorce.

Developmental histories may also be predictive of long-term outcome. To examine this possibility, developmental factors were used to predict global outcome and suicide in a study of borderline patients followed for a mean of 15 years (Paris et al. 1988). The sample was drawn from a cohort of 322 patients seen at an urban general hospital between 1958 and 1978, and, in contrast to the other three 15-year outcome studies (McGlashan 1986; Plakun et al. 1986; Stone et al. 1987), from all socioeconomic classes. Borderline diagnosis was established by Gunderson criteria (Gunderson et al. 1981) from chart review. Of the 165 patients located, 100 agreed to be interviewed. Twenty-two were deceased, 14 of these from suicide (as confirmed by coroner's records). The follow-up sample of 100 patients was shown to be clinically and demographically representative of the original cohort, and was evaluated on global outcome using the Health Sickness Rating Scale (Luborsky 1962). Of these patients, 83 had charts adequate for scoring of developmental variables.

Developmental histories were scored from charts by a rater blind to outcome, after establishing adequate interrater reliability (Paris et al. 1988). Using an index that rated common problems with parents (including chronic physical or mental illness, hypochondriasis, alcoholism, advanced age, marital conflict, parent-child conflict, under-involvement, overprotection, preoccupation, coldness, and verbal or physical abuse), summed scores were established for mother problems and father problems. Separate scores were also made for separations and losses of parent due to death and divorce, either early (ages 0 to 5) or late (ages 6 to 18). In addition, scores of 191 borderline charts were compared with scores of 39 patients admitted during the same period with diagnoses of major depression, and with retrospective DIB scores of less than 5 out of 10.

The results showed that higher scores on mother problems correlated with a poorer global outcome ($r = -.24$, $P < .05$). Neither father problems nor separation and loss correlated with outcome scores. Patients who committed suicide had fewer mother problems and fewer early separations and losses (see Table 7-1). Borderline

Table 7-1. Mean scores of developmental events in surviving and completed suicide borderline patients

	Surviving ($n = 83$)	Completed Suicide ($n = 14$)	t ($df = 90$)	P
Father problems[a]	8.6	7.5	0.87	NS
Mother problems[a]	9.5	5.1	3.23	.0002
Separation (age 0–5)[b]	0.3	0.0	4.09	.0001
Separation (age 6–18)[b]	0.9	1.2	−0.96	NS
Loss (age 0–5)[b]	0.5	0.0	5.35	.0001
Loss (age 6–18)[b]	0.5	0.6	−0.39	NS

[a]Range 0–24. [b]Range 0–2.

patients as a whole had more mother problems than depressed patients, and a marginally significant increase in early separation and loss (see Table 7-2).

DISCUSSION

The prediction of outcome by mother problems supports the hypothesis that borderline patients with more severe childhood trauma have more long-lasting interference with functioning. This finding also supports theories that emphasize the role of mothering in etiology, because problems in primary bonding affect prognosis.

It came initially as a surprise to find that borderline patients who committed suicide had somewhat better childhoods than those who survived. In a study of completed and attempted suicide, Maris (1981) found that early trauma was concentrated in attempters but not completers. On reflection, suicide can be best understood in relation to expectations in life. Those with less childhood trauma who still went on to develop borderline pathology may have found it difficult to continue living with a disorder that interferes so profoundly with interpersonal functioning. The patients who completed suicide also had higher education than those who survived (Paris et al. 1988). In a study of schizophrenic patients, Drake and Gates (1984) found that both disappointed expectations and higher education were significant predictors of completed suicide.

Finally, the excess of mother problems in borderline patients

Table 7-2. Mean scores of developmental events in borderline and nonborderline patients

	Borderline ($n = 191$)	Nonborderline ($n = 39$)	t ($df = 228$)	P
Father problems[a]	8.31	7.70	0.80	NS
Mother problems[a]	9.56	6.52	2.42	.02
Separation (age 0–5)[b]	0.54	0.46	0.49	NS
Separation (age 6–18)[b]	1.42	1.31	0.74	NS
Loss (age 0–5)[b]	0.63	0.36	1.89	.06
Loss (age 6–18)[b]	0.80	0.64	0.95	NS
Other loss (age 0–18)[b]	0.27	0.00	4.70	.0001
Total separation and loss (age 0–18)[c]	3.55	2.85	2.36	.02

[a]Range 0–24. [b]Range 0–2. [c]Range 0–10.

suggests the role of primary bonds in the etiology of the syndrome and provides concurrent validity for the developmental scoring. In this study, there was no significant excess of father problems in borderline patients, possibly reflecting the use of other hospitalized patients, rather than less severely ill outpatients, for comparison.

A recent estimate of prevalence of BPD in the community is 2% (Swartz et al. 1988). A large-scale, prospective, community follow-up study of a random sample of children could turn up enough borderline cases to provide confirmation of the empirical findings reviewed here. However, given the attrition rate to be expected from disturbed families and among the borderline patients that grow up in such families, such a project is likely to remain unrealized for some time. Alternatively, we could follow children from multiproblem families (which could be high-risk environments for creating borderline pathology) and seek to establish predictors and risk factors in the development of such children.

While waiting for more definitive data, it seems reasonable to accept what borderline patients are telling us about their families (that they are neglectful and abusive) and to conclude that family environment accounts for a good measure of the variance. Finally, it would be important, given the heterogeneity of borderline patients (Widiger and Frances 1988), to define clinically meaningful subgroups that may have different developmental pathways to becoming borderline.

REFERENCES

American Psychiatric Association: Diagnostic and Statistical Manual of Mental Disorders, 3rd Edition, Revised. Washington, DC, American Psychiatric Association, 1987

Bradley SJ: The relationship of early maternal separation to borderline personality in children and adolescents: a pilot study. Am J Psychiatry 136:424–426, 1979

Drake RE, Gates C: Suicide among schizophrenics: who is at risk? J Nerv Ment Dis 172:613–617, 1984

Feldman R, Guttman H: Families of borderline patients. Am J Psychiatry 141:1392–1396, 1984

Frank H, Hoffman N: Borderline empathy: an empirical investigation. Compr Psychiatry 27:387–395, 1987

Frank H, Paris J: Family experience in borderline patients. Arch Gen Psychiatry 38:1031–1034, 1981

Grinker R: The Borderline Syndrome. New York, Basic Books, 1968

Gunderson JG, Singer MT: Defining borderline patients. Am J Psychiatry 132:1–10, 1975

Gunderson JG, Kerr J, Englund DW: The families of borderlines: a comparative study. Arch Gen Psychiatry 37:27–33, 1980

Gunderson JG, Kolb JE, Austin KV: The diagnostic interview for borderline patients. Am J Psychiatry 138:686–692, 1981

Herman J, Perry JC, van der Kolk BA: Childhood trauma in borderline personality disorder. Am J Psychiatry 146:490–495, 1989

Links PS, Steiner M, Huxley G: The occurrence of borderline personality in the families of borderline patients. Journal of Personality Disorders 2:14–20, 1988

Luborsky L: Clinician's judgment of mental health: a proposed scale. Arch Gen Psychiatry 7:407–417, 1962

Maris R: Pathways to Suicide. Baltimore, MD, Johns Hopkins University Press, 1981

Masterson J: The Narcissistic and Borderline Disorders: An Integrated Developmental Approach. New York, Brunner/Mazel, 1981

McGlashan TH: The prediction of outcome in borderline personality disorders, in The Borderline: Current Empirical Research. Edited by McGlashan TH. Washington, DC, American Psychiatric Press, 1985, pp 61–98

McGlashan TH: The Chestnut Lodge follow-up study: III. Long-term outcome of borderline personalities. Arch Gen Psychiatry 43:1–30, 1986

Ogata S, Silk KR, Goodrich S, et al: Childhood abuse and clinical symptoms in borderline personality disorder. Paper presented at the annual meeting of the American Psychiatric Association, Montreal, May 1988

Paris J, Frank H: Perceptions of parental bonding in borderline patients. Am J Psychiatry (in press)

Paris J, Brown R, Nowlis D: Long-term follow-up of borderline patients in a general hospital. Compr Psychiatry 28:530–535, 1987

Paris J, Nowlis D, Brown R: Developmental factors in the outcome of borderline personality disorder. Compr Psychiatry 29:147–150, 1988

Paris J, Nowlis D, Brown R: Predictors of suicide in borderline patients. Can J Psychiatry 34:8–9, 1989

Plakun EM: Outcome correlates of borderline patients. Paper presented at the annual meeting of the American Psychiatric Association, Montreal, May 1988

Plakun EM, Burkhandt PE, Muller JP: Fourteen-year follow up of borderline and schizotypal personality disorders. Compr Psychiatry 26:448–455, 1986

Soloff P, Millward J: Developmental histories of borderline patients. Compr Psychiatry 23:574–588, 1983

Stone MH: The PI 500: long-term follow-up of borderline inpatients meeting DSM-III criteria. Journal of Personality Disorders 1:291–298, 1987

Stone MH, Stone DK, Hurt S: The natural history of borderline patients: I. Global Outcome. Psychiatr Clin North Am 10:185–206, 1987

Swartz MS, Zakris J, Blazer DG, et al: Estimating the prevalence of BPD in the community. Paper presented at the annual meeting of the American Psychiatric Association, Montreal, May 1988

Walsh F: Family study: fourteen new borderline cases, in The Borderline Patient. Edited by Grinker RR, Werble B. New York, Jason Aronson, 1968, pp 126–140

Widiger TA, Frances A: Personality disorders, in The American Psychiatric

130   FAMILY ENVIRONMENT AND BPD

Press Textbook of Psychiatry. Edited by Talbott JA, Hales RE, Yudofsky SC. Washington, DC, American Psychiatric Press, 1988, pp 621–648

Zanarini MC, Gunderson JG, Marino MF, et al: Childhood experiences of borderline patients. Compr Psychiatry 30:18–25, 1989

Chapter 8

Abuse and Abusiveness in Borderline Personality Disorder

Michael H. Stone, M.D.

Chapter 8

Abuse and Abusiveness in Borderline Personality Disorder

T hough the Bible admonishes us "He that spareth his rod hateth his son: but he that loveth him chasteneth him betimes" (Proverbs 13:24), in our era corporal punishment of children does not always produce the happy results King Solomon once claimed. Quite to the contrary, people of discernment see corporal punishment as neither necessary nor effective for the proper raising of children and have begun to realize that parental force, especially if clearly disproportionate to the offense and if accompanied by hostility, has "spoiled" far more children than were ever spoiled by sparing the rod. During the past generation, we have become aware of both how common parental abusiveness is in all socioeconomic classes of our country and how damaging are its effects (Strauss et al. 1980). Parental brutality, besides resulting in many deaths among infants and children, creates patterns of violence such that many abused children grow up to abuse their spouses or their own children (Brassard et al. 1987; Knutson and Mehm 1988; Van Hasselt et al. 1988).

When I first began pondering the question of etiology in borderline conditions a little over 10 years ago, I was struck by the high proportion of cases in which familial predisposition to affective disorders appeared to play a role (Stone 1977). The prevailing hypotheses until that time had emphasized psychosocial factors, especially the hampering of the separation-individuation phase of development by mothers who themselves could not tolerate their offspring's becoming emotionally separate (Masterson 1981). In recent years, I have been struck once again, as it were, this time by the histories of both physical and sexual violence in the early lives of our borderline patients.

There are several reasons why the spotlight has shifted in this fashion. One concerns a sample effect. The patients who make up the ranks of my long-term follow-up series—the PI-500—although a large sample, are nevertheless just that: a sample from a particular place and time. The PI-500 was predominantly a white, middle- to upper-middle-class, well-educated group drawn mostly from the large Protestant and Jewish population of upstate and metropolitan New York during the Vietnam years. Sexual and physical molestation within the family were not rare among our borderline patients—the incest rate was approximately 20%; the physical brutality rate about 8%—but neither were these factors as near to omnipresent as they are in other samples of borderline patients, particularly in samples gathered in this decade.

A second reason concerns the changes that have occurred over the past 8 years in diagnostic criteria. Before DSM-III (American Psychiatric Association 1980), "borderline" was mainly a label used by the psychoanalytic community, defined in broad terms that included highly impulsive or self-mutilative persons, but also included many persons in whom these attributes were absent or muted. Currently, the most popular and objectifiable definitions, those of Gunderson and Singer (1975) and DSM-III-R (American Psychiatric Association 1987), albeit polythetic, tend to single out patients who are notoriously impulsive and self-destructive. Knowing that violence begets violence, we should not be surprised, even before we begin to accumulate hard data, to learn that a history of parental violence might be more prevalent among the largely impulse-ridden borderline patients of the modern definitions than among their somewhat less abusive and impulsive counterparts of a previous generation and broader definition.

Another factor concerns cohort effects: subtle changes in representative samples of one decade for example, compared with samples from successive decades. This factor is difficult to discern even when the observer is old enough to have experienced several decades' worth of cohorts. Methodical analysis is more difficult still, because certain factors considered crucial today were scarcely thought of a generation ago, with the result that in a retrospective study the old records contain little information on key areas of current interest.

Related to the cohort factor is the investigator's theoretical stance. One's mental set will be governed by the theory to which one adheres. Inevitably, this will affect the choice of questions posed and of questions omitted. So long as separation-individuation matters were held central to the genesis of borderline conditions, clinicians inquired minutely about all issues pertinent to that factor. Because no mother is perfect, given the presence of a borderline patient, clinicians would then seize upon any crumb of evidence (or upon no crumbs at all) as proof of the mother's mishandling that phase of development. Now, we incline toward a theoretical model that emphasizes interaction of a multiplicity of hereditary, constitutional, and environmental factors, and we acknowledge the likelihood of heterogeneity; namely, that a different set of factors may be operative in one borderline patient in comparison to another.

The factor I would like to focus on here is abusiveness. I include both the abuse borderline patients may have experienced within the family during childhood and the abuse they may have directed against their own families.

The main source for my information is the PI-500: actually some 550 patients admitted to the New York State Psychiatric Institute for long-term intensive psychotherapy during the years 1963–1976 (Stone 1990b; Stone et al. 1987a, 1987b). Thus far I have traced 95% of the patients in this series. Rediagnosis by contemporary criteria yields half a dozen important subgroups: 1) borderline personality disorder (BPD) (by DSM-III), 206; 2) schizophrenic, 99; 3) schizo-affective, 64; 4) manic-depressive, 39; 5) schizophreniform psychotic, 36; and 6) borderline by Kernberg/psychostructural criteria (Kernberg 1967) but not by DSM-III, 93. The last includes 36 dysthymic patients, along with 57 patients in a mixed group, including those with antisocial personality, schizotypal personality, and anorexia/bulimia.

Other and smaller samples I have studied include those at New York Hospital and at Belmont Hospital in Brisbane, Australia (Stone et al. 1988).

THE CLINICAL DATA

In scoring the records of the PI-500, I paid attention to reports of physical abuse, whether in the form of harsh and unjustified corporal punishment or in the form of gratuitous, unprovoked assault either by a parent or by a sibling. In the absence of a control group from the normal population, I can make comparison only within the patient groups.

Table 8-1 shows the percentages of abuse victims among the various diagnostic groups. Significant differences do not emerge between these groups with respect to the incidence of parental abuse.

As for the absolute values within the groups, it is of interest that about one BPD patient in nine had an abuse history, according to the necessarily conservative estimate that can be made from chart review. Although the old records are very detailed and usually mention traumata of this sort (particularly because of the then-current tendency to blame the family for most psychopathology), the records were skimpy in some cases, and standardized trauma questionnaires were not then in use.

Borderline patients who had been the victims of parental physical abuse had on average a poorer outcome compared with borderline patients who had not been abused.

Table 8-2 shows the numbers and percentages of patients with BPD in each of six categories of outcome. Each category corresponds to a different range of the Global Assessment of Functioning Scale (GAF) as described in DSM-III-R: "suicide" corresponds to zero; "incapacitated," to scores of 1–30; "marginal," to 31–50; "fair," 51–60; "good," 61–70; and "recovered," 71 or above. For heuristic purposes, we may telescope these divisions into two broad ranges: well (scores of 61 or higher) and not well (0–60). According to this schema, the BPD patients who had not been physically abused by a parent were clinically well at 10- to 25-year follow-up in two cases out of three (118 of 174 or 67.1%). In contrast, BPD patients who had been victimized in this manner were well only in one-third of the cases (8 of 23 or 34.8%). This difference was statistically significant (χ^2 with Yates' correction = 9.12; df = 1; $P <$ .01).

The abused BPD patients were more likely than were their non-abused counterparts either to have committed suicide or to have been "incapacitated" at follow-up.

Among the parents engaging in physical abuse of their children, within the BPD domain fathers were more often involved than mothers. In five of the families, both parents participated in the abusiveness (see Table 8-3). There was no difference with respect to

Table 8-1. Victims of parental brutality

Diagnostic group	n	Victims n	%
Borderline Personality Disorder (BPD)	206	23	11.2
Comparison groups			
Borderline personality organization (but no BPD) + dysthymia	36	1	2.7
Borderline personality organization (but no BPD) + other syndromes and personality disorders	57	8	14.0
Schizophrenia	99	5	5.1
Schizoaffective	64	3	4.7
Manic-depressive	39	2	5.1
Schizophreniform	36	4	11.1

Table 8-2. BPD patients with and without a history of parental abusiveness

	Not Well				Well	
	Suicides	Incapacitated	Marginal	Fair	Good	Recovered
All traced BPD (*n* = 197) (95% traced)	17 (8.6%)	5 (2.5%)	18 (9.1%)	31 (15.7%)	51 (25.8%)	75 (38.1%)
BPD with history of parental abusiveness[a] (*n* = 23)	4 (17.4%)	4 (17.4%)	2 (8.7%)	5 (21.7%)	4 (17.4%)	4 (17.4%)
BPD without history of parental abusiveness[a] (*n* = 174)	13 (7.5%)	1 (0.57%)	16 (9.2%)	26 (14.9%)	47 (27.0%)	71 (40.1%)

[a]Well vs. not well: χ^2 = 9.62; 9.12 with Yates' correction. df = 1. $P < .01$.

Table 8-3. BPD patients with a history of parental abusiveness

Patient no.	Sex	Follow-up interval (years)[a]	Follow-up GAS	Comments
1	M	23	2	Both parents violent & provocative. Pt. killed mother 20 years after hospitalization.
2	M	20	5	Both parents extremely violent. Pt. killed 3 strangers at age 17; in jail since.
3	F	12	55	Father abusive; mother urged her to suicide.
4	F	14	30	Father threatened patient with knife.
5	M	25	56	
6	F	22	53	Father alcoholic, abusive, sexually molesting.
7	F	24	67	Father abusive.
8	F	15	68	Mother abusive.
9	F	(18)	Suicide	Father struck patient repeatedly in face for trivial "offenses."
10	F	12	70	Father abusive.
11	F	20	21	Father alcoholic, abusive. Patient later abusive to her child.
12	F	13	53	Father abusive.
13	F	25	78	Father alcoholic, agoraphobic, possessive, and abusive.
14	M	18	85	Father alcoholic and abusive.
15	F	(14)	Suicide	Stepmother violent, arrested for abuse of patient.
16	F	16	31	Father threatened patient with a gun.
17	F	25	75	Father broke patient's finger during one of many arguments.
18	F	23	82	Both parents abusive: mother, physically; father, sexually and physically.
19	F	21	63	Father abusive.
20	M	24	41	Father extremely abusive. Patient became an imposter, died in jail.
21	F	(25)	Suicide	Both parents alcoholic and abusive.
22	F	(20)	Suicide	Both parents alcoholic and abusive.
23	F	24	51	Father alcoholic and abusive.

Note. GAS = Global Assessment Scale.

[a]Parentheses indicate completed suicide.

the religious background of the abusive families when compared to those of the PI-500 as a whole, although in the Protestant and Catholic families alcoholism of one or both parents was a common accompaniment of the abusiveness (seven of nine families), whereas parental alcoholism was not noted in the abusive Jewish families (0 of a total of 14).

Because of the small numbers and because of the difficulties in quantifying the intensity, frequency, and duration of abusiveness from the old records, I cannot make an accurate estimate of the relationship between level of abuse and eventual outcome. In the five families in which both parents were distinctly abusive, the outcomes were especially abysmal. One such family consisted of two professional parents who had explosive tempers but whose underlying attitude toward the patient was positive. This patient has recovered and is successful in both home and career. But the atmosphere in the other four families was witheringly rejecting. The outcomes here have been catastrophic: two suicides, one matricide, and a mass murder.

Abusiveness Toward the Family

Among the PI-500 patients, violent acts toward a family member were common precipitants of admission to a hospital. Only occasionally were these violent acts retaliatory, in the sense of having been provoked by prior violent acts directed against the patient. The two domains—victim of abuse and perpetrator of abuse—overlapped, with respect to the BPD patients, only in half a dozen cases.

The incidence of violence toward family across all the major diagnostic groups was 10.2%. The percentages varied from zero in the dysthymic borderline patients (i.e., those with major affective disorder, Kernberg [1967] borderline features, but who did not have 5 of the DSM-III items for BPD) to 23% for the male non-DSM borderlines. The incidence was also high in the schizophreniform males (18.5%). Intergroup differences were not statistically significant, however, with the exception of a trend toward greater violence in the BPD versus dysthymic males (χ^2 = 3.64, df = 1, $P \cong$ .06). In the whole series, males were more prone to intrafamilial violence than were the females (χ^2 = 10.2, $P <$ .01). Among the borderline patients (21 with BPD plus 9 with borderline personality organization only), those who were abusive toward family members were all younger than the mean age of the whole PI-500 except for one woman whose age was precisely that of the mean age: 22. The mean age of the borderline patients who were abusive toward family was just 16 (range: 13–22), whereas the mean age of the 12 abusive schizophrenics was 23 (range: 15–35).

The family member most often victimized was the mother (38 instances), followed by the father (13) or a sibling (12). In one instance each, the victim was a wife, uncle, aunt, or grandmother. These numbers reflect the fact that some patients were abusive toward more than one family member.

The gender disproportion among abusive patients was apparent in the psychotic patients and in the non-DSM-III borderline patients. Many of the latter were antisocial; eight of nine were male. The sex ratio among the BPD group (12 female to 9 male), however, was approximately the same as among the BPD patients in general.

Outcome in the Abusive Borderline Patients

Outcome in the BPD group is essentially the same as for the BPD patients in general: median GAF = 68. Two of the males committed murder; another (who eventually committed suicide) was an arsonist. The rest largely overcame their aggressive tendencies. In some instances, their aggressive acts were limited to a period of time when they lived with abusive relatives. One girl, abandoned by her mother, was raised with her brother by a distant—and physically abusive—relative. The patient assaulted her brother on a few occasions while living in this arrangement, but has been mild mannered and tender toward this brother and now toward her own children over the 21 years since she left the unit.

The non-DSM-III borderline group contains five untraced males, four with antisocial comorbidity. The latter all came from chaotic homes. The father had abandoned the family in three cases. In the fourth, the mother was an alcoholic and violent.

Outcome in the 15 traced BPD patients with antisocial personality disorder (ASPD) comorbidity is mostly in the good-to-recovered range. The three who failed to reach this level consist of a man (alluded to earlier) from a violent home, who eventually killed his mother; a hyperkinetic adolescent who still leads a marginal existence 25 years later; and a man, brutalized by his father, who in turn assaulted his mother. This last patient has worked only sporadically at menial jobs over the past 25 years and has only meager social contacts. At the other end of the spectrum is a patient who, as an adolescent, had struck her mother but who has gone on to marry, complete an advanced degree in one of the helping professions, and administer a facility for disturbed adolescents. Her own emotionality has been well modulated for the past 20 years (current GAF = 80).

Cases in which parental violence preceded the patient's violence toward the offending parent(s) or toward other family members encourage one to make the equation "violence breeds violence." In the general population, where studies on a very large scale are possible, this equation probably is valid (Gelles and Strauss 1988). But the violence is not always visited upon the parents; many abused children somehow refrain from committing acts of violence against family members or outsiders. Only 6 of the 21 BPD patients had a history of assaultiveness toward family and had been the victims of parental brutality; the rest have not been violent toward anyone; two of the six were abusive toward children.

With regard to the PI-500, there is strong evidence that parental brutality has, on average, a deleterious impact on the life course of the abused children. There is less evidence that this necessarily induces retaliatory violence against the offending parent(s) or that the life course of borderline patients who have behaved assaultively toward a parent is poorer than the group average, unless the home environment was particularly chaotic or violent. In the latter situation, the factor determining poor outcome would appear to be the chronically destructive environment itself and not the mere fact that on occasion the child had struck a parent or a sibling.

Incest

The topic of intrafamilial sexual abuse within the PI-500 has been addressed in several recent papers (Stone 1989a, 1990a; Stone et al. 1988). Incest histories were more common among the BPD females (28 of 145, 19.3%) than among the schizophrenic females (2 of 39, 5.2%). The schizoaffective females also had a high incidence rate (11 of 41, 26.8%). Male BPD patients reported incestuous experiences in 10% of cases (6 of 61). Two of the latter involved seduction by the mother and terminated in the suicides of the two sons. Among the females, outcomes were not significantly different from those of female BPD patients who had not been incest victims unless the involved relative was a father, in which case there was a tendency toward worse than average outcome.

CLINICAL DATA FROM OTHER CENTERS

Two years ago I had the opportunity of interviewing directly patients admitted to an inpatient unit in Brisbane, Australia, devoted to the long-term psychotherapy of borderline and other personality-disordered patients. Fifteen patients (14 female and 1 male) met criteria for BPD. Ages ranged from 14 to 40 years (average 28), socioeconomic status from II to IV. Physical, sexual, and intense verbal abuse within the family was common in this group. Thirteen of the 15 had experienced at least one form of abuse. The most frequently noted were verbal (73%), physical, and sexual (47%). The latter could be divided into incest (47%) and extrafamilial (40%). The figures take into account that 12 patients had suffered more than one type of trauma.

The incest rate among 29 BPD females at New York Hospital-Westchester Division, interviewed the same year as the Australian sample, was 35%; the physical abuse rate was 28%.

CLINICAL EXAMPLES

The raw statistics alone do not convey the vividness of the abuse picture in borderline patients. Furthermore, restriction to physical and verbal forms of abuse would fail to cover the whole spectrum of hurtful interactions. Some borderline patients, for example, were the recipients of exquisite psychological humiliation or torture, as in the case of a borderline woman at New York Hospital whose mother, by way of expressing disapproval of a boyfriend, served her daughter a sandwich buttered with the mother's feces. The mother of a borderline woman in Brisbane was a religious fanatic obsessed with keeping her daughter "pure." To this end, she would lock her in a closet without food the day before the Sabbath so as to leave the eliminatory organs cleansed. Upon releasing her daughter in time for church, this woman would first scrub her daughter's vulva with steel wool, the better to prepare that area for the holy day. Not surprisingly, the patient, who added self-mutilations to the injuries inflicted by her mother, developed an *idée fixe* to the effect that she had a "real," and loving, mother somewhere in the outback, and that the abusive parent was merely an imposter.

The father of one of the PI-500 was a man with an explosive personality who frequently struck his daughter in the face full force for various peccadillos, sometimes for nothing at all. Moments later, he would hug her and reassure her she was his favorite. She tortured animals as a youngster, and in her adult life indulged in satanic witchcraft practices with her first husband. She also molested other people's children, for which she was arrested and jailed. Hospitalized 11 times, she committed suicide after her third husband left her.

A borderline outpatient at Beth Israel Hospital behaved sadistically toward his girlfriend and menacingly toward his therapist. Both his parents were alcoholic and abusive. His father, to curb his son's crying at age 4, would hold him upside down by his ankles outside the window of their 12th story apartment, yelling, "If you don't shut up, I'll let go!"

A borderline women at the same clinic came from a wealthy home in New England in which she witnessed at 13 her father kill her mother with a rifle, warning his daughter, "If you tell the police, I'll kill you too." This woman seemed bent on destroying herself without her father's help via promiscuity, drug abuse, and affairs with criminals.

Three of the borderline women in the PI-500 were witnesses to their fathers' savage beatings of their brothers; in another instance, brother and sister alike were beaten. In one of these families, two of the brothers committed suicide, as did the patient herself some years later.

A borderline man from the PI-500 study had been physically abused on a regular basis by his stepmother. To get away from his family, he settled in the South after leaving the hospital, living as a day-worker and vagrant, never contacting his father. After the death of this stepmother, the father retired in the South to a town 10 miles away. Father and son were (and remain to this day) unaware of each other's proximity.

One of the BPD males in the PI-500 came from a family in which most of the males were violence prone. Both his parents were physically and verbally abusive to each other and to him. As a child he was markedly hyperactive and uncontrollable. He set fires, struck other children at school, and was admitted to a psychiatric center because of his conduct disturbance. At 17, he joined the army, having reported his age as 18. On a weekend pass, he returned home to find his father battering his mother. He thrust his rifle under his father's chin, threatening to press the trigger if he did not desist. This calmed the father but not the patient, who shortly thereafter killed three people in a restaurant, for which he has been in prison over the past 17 years.

DISCUSSION

The role of violence in the pathogenesis of BPD is difficult to assess. Severe abuse by primary caregivers is often present in the histories of borderline patients. It remains unclear whether we are entitled to claim specificity for such abuse in the development of BPD, because abuse histories of similar magnitude are noted in the backgrounds of patients with antisocial, avoidant, and other personality disorders. Similar histories are a regular feature in cases of multiple personality (Kluft 1985). In the PI-500, there was a trend toward greater frequency of abuse history in the BPD than in the schizophrenic patients. This tendency would have reached the customary confidence level in statistical analysis ($P < .05$) had 25 instead of 23 BPD patients experienced abuse during their formative years. Because my estimate relied on chart review rather than on personal interview, it is possible that additional cases would have come to light had a more direct method been uniformly feasible.

Although parental abusiveness cuts across socioeconomic lines and is found in all social classes, the frequency appears to be higher in lower-middle-class than in upper-class families (Strauss et al. 1980). In psychiatric facilities serving primarily lower-middle-class populations, a history of parental abuse might be common, and equally so, in all diagnostic categories. If this were so, one might argue that abuse was "causative" with respect to BPD but merely "contributory" toward the development of conditions like schizophrenia or mania, for which genetic/constitutional influences loom larger in the causal hierarchy. Until better epidemiological studies are carried out concerning abuse histories across a wide spectrum of personality disorders, we cannot say with certainty whether caregiver abusiveness is more common in personality-disordered patients than in those with the functional psychoses or more common in BPD (and probably in ASPD) than in, for example, obsessive-compulsive and passive-dependent personality disorders. It may be that abusiveness will emerge as an important but nonspecific factor.

Until more data are accumulated, we are left with clinical impressions and the hypotheses they generate. My own impressions lead me to postulate that severe caregiver abuse—especially where physical, verbal, and sexual abuse occur together, with regularity, and within an atmosphere of dislike and rejection—is a significant causative factor for those personality disorders characterized by impulsivity. Given the greater proneness to violence in males than in females (presumably on a biological basis), the impact of caregiver abusiveness might have a different range of expression between the genders, emerging more often as BPD among exposed females and as ASPD among exposed males. I have expressed this belief elsewhere (Stone 1988), in which I attempted to show how the DSM-III items that make up the BPD diagnosis may each arise on a posttraumatic as well as on a constitutional basis. Kolb's concepts (1987) of posttraumatic stress disorder and of its genesis are useful in outlining possible links between early traumata and subsequent disorders, especially those of impulse and affect.

With respect to sexual abuse, Russell (1986) suggested that incest may be more prevalent in this generation than in previous ones, perhaps because of such factors as the breakdown of the traditional family leaving a higher proportion of young girls in divorce homes where the head of the household is a stepfather rather than biologic father. However this may be, sexual abuse, especially within the family and by a member of the older generation, appears particularly powerful as a causative factor in the evolution of borderline conditions.

The data pertaining to violence and to extreme forms of humiliation, verbal abuse, and psychological torment are not adequate to permit comparisons between generations. Although violence seems to be on the increase in America (Plutchik 1988), we are becoming increasingly aware of it, hence more apt to inquire about it in the lives of our patients.

Many of the borderline patients in the PI-500 with a history of abusiveness had childhood histories of abuse. Nevertheless, one cannot predict that a history of physical abuse regularly leads to abusive behavior. Sometimes one sees impulsivity of other sorts (promiscuity, running away, stealing, drug abuse). It is probably nearer the truth to say that incest and severe parental abuse alter the recipient's nervous system to become less capable of modulation and more prone to immediate uncontrolled responses—in a word, more impulsive (Frosch 1977). We know from other epidemiological work that young runaways are very likely to have been abused sexually, corporally, or both; many already show the traits of BPD.

We also know that some severely abused children who have gone on to develop BPD, and with it some aggressive behavior, eventually outgrow their impulsivity and proneness to aggression. In the PI-500, this more favorable evolution was apt to occur in borderline females with mild antisocial tendencies (truancy, lying, shoplifting), who, as they approached 30, were able to shift into healthier, more adaptive patterns of behavior. A small number of abused and neglected males who had become delinquent as teenagers and borderline as young adults were also able to give up their antisociality in their 30s. These were the nonassaultive males. Their more aggressive and violence-prone counterparts have remained either grossly dysfunctional or untraced. The abused and mildly antisocial borderline patients who did improve seldom did so in relation to psychotherapy. Their good outcome seemed to have to do with nonspecific or chance factors: delayed maturation, rescue by friends who had them join one of the many "Anonymous" groups, religious conversion, and the like.

It remains to be seen whether the gender parity I noted in the PI-500 borderline patients who acted abusively toward their family members is true of other borderline samples. One would anticipate a male preponderance. Maqueda (1988) noted a significant male excess in adolescents who sought counseling because of having assaulted their mothers, but this author did not report on the diagnostic or personality disorder categories to which his patients belonged. Most of Maqueda's patients were the sons of divorced, father-absent families. In this respect, they resembled the non-DSM-III borderline/antisocial males in my series who had assaulted their mothers.

Four-fifths of the abusive BPD patients, in contrast, came from intact, albeit often chaotic, families.

If we are to progress from the correlational stage in our observation of frequent parental abusiveness in BPD patients toward an assessment of its possible causative significance, we will need standardized measures of abusiveness in large samples of patients with borderline and other personality disorders. We will need quantifiable data on the frequency, intensity, timing, and accompanying attitude of the parents' abuse as well as some measure of the parents' general attitude (loving, rejecting, indifferent). With the help of several colleagues, I have recently carried out a reliability study of a scale we developed for this purpose: The Lifetime Inventory of Traumatic Events (LITE) (Gallagher et al. 1989). Of equal importance will be the establishment of a parental abusiveness "baseline," that is, the frequency (and so forth) of abusiveness in the histories of normal controls. How likely are persons from the general population, free of psychiatric disorder, to have suffered parental abuse of the magnitude reported by BPD and other personality-disordered patients? What is the greatest degree of such abuse still compatible with a psychologically healthy adaptation? We will want to disentangle as best we can "nature" from "nurture" influences. How often do abusive parents of future BPD patients themselves suffer from affective disorders, alcoholism, and so forth? How often does BPD arise in families in which abusiveness exists in "pure culture"? How often do we confront dual-factor situations where, for example, an abusive, bipolar-manic father has burdened a child with both the risk-genes and the psychological stresses that might lead to the irritable/impulsive traits we later identify as "borderline"?

Whatever the outcome of these studies in the future, we need to recognize in the here and now that the parental abusiveness factor, when present in the history of a borderline patient, must be taken into account in shaping treatment recommendations. Severely traumatized patients often need a great deal in the way of support, sanctuary, sealing over, and specialized forms of group therapy (an anonymous group devoted to victims of physical or sexual abuse). Analytically oriented exploration of the traumatic experiences, especially where they have been harrowing or grotesque, must often be postponed for a long time, until some strengthening of the personality and some measurable improvement in the areas of work and socialization have occurred. In the most severely traumatized borderline patients, exploratory therapy would, at any time, provide too intense a reliving of terror and other overwhelming emotions; in such patients this form of therapy would be contraindicated.

REFERENCES

American Psychiatric Association: Diagnostic and Statistical Manual of Mental Disorders, 3rd Edition. Washington, DC, American Psychiatric Association, 1980

American Psychiatric Association: Diagnostic and Statistical Manual of Mental Disorders, 3rd Edition, Revised. Washington, DC, American Psychiatric Association, 1987

Brassard MR, Germain R, Hart SN (eds): Psychological Maltreatment of Children and Youth. New York, Pergamon, 1987

Frosch J: Disorders of impulse control. Psychiatry 40:295–314, 1977

Gallagher R, Hurt S, Flye B, et al: The Lifetime Inventory of Traumatic Events (LITE): a reliability study. Unpublished manuscript, 1989

Gelles RJ, Strauss MA: Intimate Violence. New York, Simon & Schuster, 1988

Gunderson JG, Singer MT: Defining borderline patients: an overview. Am J Psychiatry 132:1–10, 1975

Kernberg OF: Borderline personality organization. J Am Psychoanal Assoc 15:641–685, 1967

Kluft RP: Childhood Antecedents of Multiple Personality. Washington, DC, American Psychiatric Press, 1985

Knutson JF, Mehm JC: Transgenerational patterns of coercion in families and intimate relationships, in Violence in Intimate Relationships. Edited by Russell GW. New York, PMA Publishing, 1988, pp 67–90

Kolb LC: A neuropsychological hypothesis explaining post-traumatic stress disorders. Am J Psychiatry 144:989–995, 1987

Maqueda F: Coups de fil pour coups de fils: recontres dans une permanence avec des meres battues par leurs enfants adolescents. L'Information Psychiatrique 64:909–915, 1988

Masterson J: Borderline and Narcissistic Disorders. New York, Brunner/Mazel, 1981

Plutchik R: Suicide and violence. Paper presented at the Middletown Psychiatric Center, Middletown, NY, November 1988

Russell DC: The Secret Trauma. New York, Basic Books, 1986

Stone MH: The borderline syndrome: evolution of the term, genetic aspects and prognosis. Am J Psychother 31:345–365, 1977

Stone MH: Toward a psychobiological theory of borderline conditions. Dissociation 1:1–15, 1988

Stone MH: Individual psychotherapy with victims of incest. Psychiatr Clin North Am 12:237–255, 1989a

Stone MH: Incest in the borderline patient, in Incest-Related Syndromes of Adult Psychopathology. Edited by Kluft RP. Washington, DC, American Psychiatric Press, 1990a

Stone MH: The Fate of Borderline Patients. New York, Guilford Press, 1990b

Stone MH, Hurt S, Stone DK: Natural history of borderline patients treated by intensive hospitalization. Psychiatr Clin North Am 10:185–206, 1987a

Stone MH, Stone DK, Hurt S: The PI-500: long-term follow-up of borderline in-patients meeting DSM-III criteria. Journal of Personality Disorders 1:291–298, 1987b

Stone MH, Unwin A, Beacham B, et al: Incest in female borderlines: its frequency and impact. International Journal of Family Psychiatry 9:277–293, 1988

Strauss MA, Gelles RJ, Steinmetz SK: Behind Closed Doors: Violence in the American Family. Garden City, NJ, Anchor Books, 1980

Van Hasselt VB, Morrison RL, Bellack AS, et al (eds): Handbook of Family Violence. New York, Plenum, 1988

Chapter 9

New Perspectives on Becoming Borderline

John G. Gunderson, M.D.

Chapter 9

New Perspectives on Becoming Borderline

It is both an honor and a challenge to discuss the complicated chapters in this volume and the attendant issues of the pathogenesis of borderline personality disorder (BPD). By necessity, this discussion reflects a very selective account of the many studies related to this subject that have appeared in the past decade (Gunderson and Zanarini 1988). In a general way, this book illuminates both the contributions and the limitations of a succession of etiological theories that have focused attention on bad parenting, biogenetic failures, and stressful events. I will first highlight a few issues, namely, the ongoing search for familial pedigree linkages, the burgeoning evidence of a role for abuse, and the growth in appreciation for enduring social disablers. I will then explore the implications for the future that I foresee can be derived from this research.

FAMILIAL PEDIGREE LINKAGES

The examination of the relatives of borderline patients to assess the aggregation of borderline and other psychiatric disorders is a particularly important subject. The independence of such observation from the index patient makes it an especially credible form of validation, and the findings clearly bear on the subject of transmissibility. Both Zanarini et al. (Chapter 4) and Links et al. (1988a) offer family prevalence data that document a high frequency of borderline personality in the relatives of borderline patients. This is particularly notable insofar as it gives additional methodologically improved evidence to support the validity of this personality disorder. At the same time, as highlighted by Segal (Chapter 2), this finding harkens back to Masterson's emphasis on traumatic separation disturbances as central to his use of the borderline term, and it contrasts to the more ancillary role that traumatic separations are given by the other theorists Segal cites. However, despite the higher than normal frequency of BPD in the mothers, the data cannot be reduced to

Masterson's conclusion. Links' study (Links et al. 1988a) indicates that even when BPD was found within the family pedigrees, it was not predominantly due to the mothers. Both the Zanarini et al. (Chapter 4) and Ogata et al. (Chapter 5) studies also note that many mothers have other kinds of psychopathology. In any event, borderline pathology seems to have a familial link, which is an argument for the validity of the disorder. Moreover, these studies along with Paris (Chapter 7) and Stone (Chapter 8) dispel the belief in the specific pathogenic impact of early, prolonged, and traumatic parental separations or losses. They seem not to be a necessary or sufficient factor to explain this disorder's origins.

Equally interesting and potentially more important is the suggestion from three of these studies (Chapters 4, 5, and 6) that borderline patients may have familial linkages with other disorders. These studies suggest there is an increase of substance abuse, alcoholism, and antisocial personality in the relatives of borderline patients. Such results heavily underscore the linkage, previously noted by others (Andrulonis and Vogel 1984; Loranger and Tulis 1985; Soloff and Millward 1983), of BPD to underlying psychopathology associated with impulsivity. Although this familial linkage to impulsivity is observably environmental in nature, it is certainly plausible that genetic transmission is also operative. Regardless, the linkage to impulsivity points biogenetic researchers toward substrates deserving their attention, such as the dopaminergic (Cloninger 1987) or serotonergic (Siever et al. 1985) systems. Whether the familial transmission is via biogenetic or social paths, the link to impulsivity is a departure from the earlier studies, which initially looked for linkages to schizophrenia and then, under the leadership of Stone and Akiskal, began to look for linkages to the affective disorders.

The analysis by Zanarini et al. (Chapter 4) is a particularly revealing one in connection to the linkage of BPD and affective disorder. Much of the apparent increase of affective disorder among the relatives was found to be contingent upon whether the borderline cohort member had concurrent affective disorder. This result echoes other family history studies that have separated out borderline probands without concurrent affective disorder (Andrulonis and Vogel 1984; Pope et al. 1983). This observation is joined by recent work that shows that other personality types also have an increased prevalence of affectively disordered relatives (Shea et al. 1987) and that borderline patients are not particularly responsive to tricyclic antidepressants (Soloff et al. 1986). Such findings do not dismiss the idea of borderline personality as being linked to affective disorders, but they greatly diminish the likelihood that such a linkage is specific and that it is very explanatory.

SEXUAL/PHYSICAL ABUSE

Ogata et al.'s (Chapter 5) results indicate that a remarkable 71% of the borderline cohort had a history of sexual abuse compared with about 22% for the depressive cohort. These results now join those of other investigators (Herman and van der Kolk 1987; Links et al. 1988b; Stone 1987; Zanarini et al. 1989) who also have documented how widespread sexual abuse is in the backgrounds of borderline patients. Such results have underscored the etiologic significance of incest and physical abuse in particular while, more generally, linking BPD to posttraumatic stress disorder (PTSD).

A colleague, who recently commented on this association of BPD and sexual abuse, exclaimed, "How could people who have studied or treated borderline patients for any length of time have ignored or overlooked this incredible preponderance of abuse in their backgrounds?" (I took it personally because I am among those people described by Segal [Chapter 2] whose theorizing failed to give abuse the attention it very clearly deserves.) Stone (Chapter 8) suggests four rationalizations. First, he indicates that the rate of abuse may be as low as 11%. (That rate reduces the level of irresponsibility in underestimating this factor by prior observers!) Moreover, Stone notes that similar histories of abuse were found in other diagnostic samples and, if borne out by other studies, point to a more nonspecific role vis-à-vis the origins of borderline personality than has been postulated by some investigators. Second, it may be that sexual abuse did not receive due attention because earlier studies used a broad definition of the borderline disorder. As it has become defined as a specific type of personality disorder, borderline disorder now prototypically includes a more impulse-ridden group in whom a background of abuse may be more predominant. A third reason offered by Stone derives from the fact that sexual and physical abuse is more common in the background of lower socioeconomic groups. Because patients in psychoanalytic psychotherapy were the sources for much of the original theorizing about etiology that Segal aptly summarizes (Chapter 2), this sample was especially unlikely to have such histories. It may even be that a history of sexual or physical abuse is a factor in its own right that would cause even socioeconomically advantaged clients to avoid or discontinue intensive therapy. Certainly such people are likely to find both unstructured and intensively exploratory therapies very frightening. Finally, Stone cites Russell (1986), who has proposed that abuse may be rising in the current era as a by-product of increasingly common broken homes and stepparenting.

It is safe to say that there is a great deal more awareness, both within psychiatry and among the public, about sexual abuse. Within psychiatry, greater awareness has made sexual abuse a more routine part of evaluations. The public attention makes patients much more likely to volunteer information about it. No doubt, earlier generations of clinicians were more prone to overestimate the danger of retrospective unconscious distortions. Now the risk may be that clinicians too naively assume the traumatic impact of retrospective reports. This, as Ogata et al. (Chapter 5) point out, is particularly possible in borderline patients. Borderline persons have both an increased capacity for distorted perceptions and strong motivations for vilifying past caregivers. A recent change in the Medical Practices Act in Minnesota highlights this hazard. Because of public concern about sexual abuse, the statute combines with support groups to encourage patients to request disciplinary actions against those physicians whose conduct or words are "seductive or sexually demeaning" (C. Malmquist, December 1988, personal communication). Many clinicians are already reluctant to treat BPD; this shift would make such treatments masochistic. This is paradoxically likely to inhibit clinicians from confronting misattributions rather than making them more aggressive in correcting such impressions that borderline patients can readily develop.

Both Stone (Chapter 8) and Paris (Chapter 7) provide the first reports to relate background factors to prognosis for borderline samples. Stone's report documents that past abuse worsens the prognosis (one-third completed suicide or were incapacitated); Paris offers a different perspective on predicting suicide. His report shows that suicide was associated with fewer problems in either mothering or in early separation/loss experiences. I agree with his explanation that higher socioeconomic backgrounds and other cultural factors may have given higher expectations to the people who suicided. Patients with pride are more of a suicide risk. Also, higher education might reflect a better ability to organize data and think clearly, which might also have made them confront painful realities. Disorganization or perceptual distortions at critical times may serve defensive functions for borderline patients that are less available to the group with higher socioeconomic backgrounds. In any event, both the Stone and the Paris studies are creative entries that elaborate new clinical significance for historical information. In the years to come, these reports doubtlessly will stimulate similar studies done by others.

ENDURING SOCIAL DISABLERS

The impressive familial linkage to impulsivity documented in the work by Zanarini et al. (Chapter 4), Ogata et al. (Chapter 5), and Links et al. (Chapter 6) establishes that a modern theory for the pathogenesis of borderline personality must add emphasis that may help account for impulsivity. The present research underscores the ongoing exposures to impulsive and often aggressive behaviors of the parents, which almost certainly provide modeling behavior and prompt maladaptive identifications. These exposures take place throughout development and call for a model of pathogenesis that gives greater emphasis to such ongoing social learning experiences as have been highlighted recently by Millon (1987). Such work supports the earlier criticisms of psychoanalytic models that suggest that the origins of adult borderline psychopathology are phase-specific or are determined before the age of 3 or 4 years (Gunderson 1987). The importance of advancing the weight given to enduring social factors is not that it diminishes the role that trauma (e.g., separations or abuse) can have on development, but that it prevents oversight of the social context in which such traumata occur and that renders them so distinctly pathogenic.

The absence of appropriate supports in the form of stable structures, soothing presences, active nurture or able substitutes within the ongoing family matrix may be more important than trauma in determining the development of a borderline personality. Such issues are harder to document and validate by researchers and harder to recognize, distinguish, and articulate by patients. In this regard, Ogata et al.'s (Chapter 5) use of Moos' Family Environment Scale (FES) (Moos and Moos 1981) is a welcome effort to document this aspect of the pathogenesis of borderline personality. The results confirm clinical impressions and what can be logically deduced from the studies on psychopathology in the parents. The families of borderline patients have far more angry conflict and far less organization and supportive cohesion. These observations on the families of borderline patients have been independently confirmed with different samples by Johnson et al. (1989). This may be a particularly toxic family background when it is combined with little opportunity to express feelings and expectations of normal independence, achievement, and morality. Children are encouraged to measure themselves by standards against which they always fail and that they are ill-prepared to pursue. These studies also document the early school problems of preborderline children. Rather than simply a symptom of their handicaps, such performance problems become a factor in their own right in perpetuating the inner sense of badness, the sense of social alienation, and the pathetic search for supportive attention, which eventually become the hallmarks of adult borderline psychopathology.

A scholarly review of efforts to assess the intrapsychic and interpersonal handicaps of borderline patients is found in the chapter by

Marziali and Munroe Blum (Chapter 3). It offers the hope that future longitudinal studies will identify the developmental paths by which such core aspects of borderline psychopathology evolve and how they interact with the social conditions found in such patients' homes, schools, and recreational settings. There is no doubt in my mind that institutions and social structures outside the home can have very powerful effects in diminishing the pathogenic force of both familial trauma and the ongoing familial conflicts and disorganization. Only prospective evaluations of high-risk children (e.g., those with disturbed mothers, traumatic separations and abuse, and broken families) can illustrate the ways in which social cultural factors outside the family augment or derail the development of borderline psychopathology.

SUMMARY AND IMPLICATIONS

The studies and reviews contained in this book point to heterogeneity in the pathogenesis of BPD. Moreover, these studies indicate that the etiology of this disorder, when examined carefully, moves one into a systems model. Not the initial etiologic models, derived by clinicians, that emphasized pathological early interactions with parents nor the second generation of models, offered by academicians, about a genetically controlled temperament or a biological vulnerability nor the third model, which emphasizes past traumatic stressors, is capable by itself of unlocking the etiologic puzzle. The studies on traumatic impact of early separations, the modeling effects of emotionally and impulsively disturbed parents, and the effects of sustained abuse join the studies on family pedigrees in pointing to heterogeneous backgrounds of borderline patients. There are multiple factors that can help shape the borderline patient's personality, but none are likely to be very specific and they are likely to have additive effects.

Studies of psychopathology often follow a sequence of trying to define a syndrome, then determining whether that syndrome can be differentiated from others. The next wave of studies often follows cohorts of patients longitudinally to see whether they are stable or whether they change in consistent and homogeneous patterns. Retrospective reconstructions and family history studies such as those recorded in this book are often the next stage. This group of studies, in turn, sets the stage for the next wave of studies, which will include more prospective evaluations of these same factors using high-risk cohorts and twin or adoptive studies to get more definitive answers about etiology. Even before such more definitive strategies are undertaken, the present studies draw attention to important issues that can and should be explored. Among these are the following five:

1. Evaluate the biological and neurological effects in early life of
   a. traumatic separation
   b. prolonged exposure to chaotic and conflictual families
   c. physical and sexual abuse
2. Quantify the severity of parental separations or losses with consideration for
   a. maternal versus paternal
   b. age of onset, frequency, and duration
   c. relation to marital conflict
   d. relation to conflicts over parental role
   e. presence/absence of alternative parenting sources
3. Quantify the severity of different forms of sexual/physical abuse in relation to
   a. parental versus other relatives versus nonfamily
   b. age of onset, frequency, and duration
   c. violent versus submissive versus sought
   d. types of abusive activity
4. Evaluate whether a history of traumatic separations, family conflict, and abusiveness in diagnosed borderline patients has implications upon their
   a. prognosis
   b. descriptive characteristics (e.g., tolerance of being alone, in stability of relationships, and dissociation, respectively)
   c. response to medications (e.g., monoamine oxidase inhibitors, benzodiazepines, and phenothiazines, respectively)
5. Evaluate whether a familial aggregation of cognitive, affective, or impulsive disorders in diagnosed borderline patients has implications for their
   a. prognosis
   b. descriptive characteristics (e.g., reality testing, anger, and impulsivity, respectively)
   c. response to pharmacotherapies (e.g., phenothiazines, tricyclic antidepressants, and carbamazepine, respectively)

   In conclusion, it is worth noting that diagnosis should increasingly become the handmaiden to etiology within psychiatry as it is elsewhere in medicine. The most far-reaching impact of the greater diagnostic specificity introduced by DSM-III (American Psychiatric Association 1980) and DSM-III-R (American Psychiatric Association 1987) has been to foster research and comparability between studies. This increased research has already stimulated helpful explorations into the etiologic factors that lie behind syndromes. This book illustrates some directions in which the examinations of pathogenesis can lead to the borderline diagnosis. The work implicating the role of serious sexual/physical abuse indicates that, in the future, a few patients now diagnosed as having BPD may better be diagnosed as having PTSD, specifically, those whose personality was not already deeply scarred before sustained abuse and whose personality changes when removed from abusive circumstances. Likewise, the work implicating the role of underlying affective dysregulation indicates that a small subgroup of patients now called borderline may better be diagnosed as having affective disorder, specifically, those whose underlying affective vulnerability is revealed when their impulsivity, separation fears, and manipulativeness dramatically disappear along with their dysphoria in response to antidepressant medications. The research into pathogenesis also shows that such divisions are unlikely to affect the vast majority of those now identified as BPD. For them, the clinical impact of research such as this is to set healthy limits on the search for etiologic simplification. These results make plain that multimodal and long-term treatments will be needed to address the multiple and long-sustained factors whose interactions give rise to this disorder.

REFERENCES

American Psychiatric Association: Diagnostic and Statistical Manual of Mental Disorders, 3rd Edition. Washington, DC, American Psychiatric Association, 1980

American Psychiatric Association: Diagnostic and Statistical Manual of Mental Disorders, 3rd Edition, Revised. Washington, DC, American Psychiatric Association, 1987

Andrulonis PA, Vogel NG: Comparison of borderline personality subcategories to schizophrenic and affective disorders. Br J Psychiatry 144:358–363, 1984

Cloninger CR: A systematic method for clinical description and classification of personality variants. Arch Gen Psychiatry 44:573–588, 1987

Gunderson JG: Interfaces between psychoanalytic and empirical studies of borderline personality, in The Borderline Patient: Emerging Concepts in Diagnosis, Psychodynamics, and Treatment. Edited by Grotstein JS, Solomon MF, Lang JA. Hillsdale, NJ, Analytic Press, 1987, pp 37–60

Gunderson JG, Zanarini MC: Pathogenesis of borderline personality, in American Psychiatric Press Review of Psychiatry, Vol 8. Edited by Tasman S, Hales RE, Frances AJ. Washington, DC, American Psychiatric Press, 1988, pp 25–48

Herman J, van der Kolk BA: Traumatic antecedents of borderline personality disorder, in Psychological Trauma. Edited by van der Kolk BA. Washington, DC, American Psychiatric Press, 1987, pp 111–126

Johnson C, Tobin D, Enright MA: Prevalence and clinical characteristics of borderline patients in an eating-disordered population. J Clin Psychiatry 50:9–15, 1989

Links PS, Steiner M, Huxley G: The occurrence of borderline personality disorder in the families of borderline patients. Journal of Personality Disorders 2:14–20, 1988a

Links PS, Steiner M, Offord DR, et al: Characteristics of borderline personality disorder: a Canadian study. Can J Psychiatry 33:336–340, 1988b

Loranger AW, Tulis EH: Family history of alcoholism in borderline personality disorder. Arch Gen Psychiatry 42:153–157, 1985

Masterson JF: Treatment of the Borderline Adolescent: A Developmental Approach. New York, Wiley Interscience, 1972

Moos R, Moos B: Family Environment Scale Manual. Palo Alto, CA, Consulting Psychologists Press, 1981

Pope HG, Jonas JM, Hudson JI, et al: The validity of DSM-III borderline personality disorder. Arch Gen Psychiatry 40:23–30, 1983

Russell DE: The Secret Trauma. New York, Basic Books, 1986

Shea MT, Glass DR, Pilkonis PA, et al: Frequency and implications of personality disorders in a sample of depressed outpatients. Journal of Personality Disorders 1:27–42, 1987

Siever LJ, Klar H, Coccaro E: Psychobiologic substrates of personality, in Biologic Response Styles: Clinical Implications. Edited by Klar H, Siever LJ. Washington, DC, American Psychiatric Press, 1985, pp 38–66

Soloff PH, Millward JW: Psychiatric disorders in the families of borderline patients. Arch Gen Psychiatry 40:37–44, 1983

Soloff PH, George A, Nathan RS, et al: Progress in pharmacotherapy of borderline disorders. Arch Gen Psychiatry 43:691–697, 1986

Stone MH: The Borderline Syndromes. New York, McGraw-Hill, 1987

Zanarini MC, Gunderson JG, Marino MF, et al: Childhood experiences of borderline patients. Compr Psychiatry 30:18–25, 1989